ALTERNATIVES
New Approaches to Health, Education, Energy, the Family and the Aquarian Age

The earth does not belong to man; man belongs to the earth. This we know. All things are connected like the blood which unites one family. Whatever befalls the earth befalls the sons of the earth. Man did not weave the web of life; he is merely a strand in it. Whatever he does to the web, he does to himself.

Chief Seattle, Suguamish Tribe, 1854.

ALTERNATIVES

New Approaches to Health, Education, Energy, the Family and the Aquarian Age

John Osmond and Angela Graham

A companion to the *HTV* series

THORSONS PUBLISHERS LIMITED

ALTERNATIVES
is published by
THORSONS PUBLISHERS
LIMITED
Denington Estate, Wellingborough,
Northamptonshire NN8 2RQ

© HTV Limited 1984

Published August 1984;
reprinted September 1984

Designed and produced by
Michael Balfour Ltd
3 Wedgwood Mews,
Greek Street, London W1V 5LW

Designer: Hilly Beavan
Typesetting: H & J Graphics Ltd
Printed in Great Britain by
Fletcher & Son Ltd, Norwich

British Library Cataloguing in
Publication Data

Osmond, John
    Alternatives,
    1. Subculture
    I. Title II. Graham, Angela
    306'.1   HM73

    ISBN 0-7225-1138-8

Cover: *A Cretan windmill erected amidst the mountains at the Centre for Alternative Technology, Machynlleth, Wales. It can generate up to 700 watts of electricity but is most often used for pumping or lathe and grindstone work.*

Half-title: *Play time on the turf roof of Ty Cwrdd Bach.*

Title page: *This house in Milton Keynes is part of an energy-conscious housing estate. It uses both 'passive' and 'active' solar heating.*

Contents page: *The HTV crew that filmed the series ALTERNATIVES. From right to left: Paul Gaydon, sound recordist; John Roberts, director; Shân Hughes Davies, production assistant; Mick Reynolds, cameraman; Eric Balicki, assistant cameraman; and the authors of the book, Angela Graham, researcher, and John Osmond, editor of the series. Many more people contributed to the television series, in particular the film editor Steve Paull and his assistant Roger Mitchell. The series was produced under the executive direction of Geraint Talfan Davies.*

CONTENTS

PREFACE

This book and the television series on which it is based have been two years in the making. As we say in our opening chapter, we did not set out with the idea of making a series of programmes, and least of all writing a book about them. But it is of the very essence of alternative activity and thinking that one thing leads to another until, like the threads of an interwoven fabric, the whole appears. We have been fascinated to discover that just beneath the surface of society in Britain today is evolving a whole new fabric that makes up the Alternative Movement. And it has appeared to us as an evolutionary process: the new growing within the faded structures of the old.

It will be immediately obvious that we have been very taken by much of the Alternative Movement and its thinking. We have adopted an essentially descriptive approach and not attempted a critical analysis. This we feel necessary, but a more immediate need is for a wider public to become aware of the Alternative Movement and its message. This was the main reason we produced the television series and this book.

No book of this kind can present a definitive survey. The alternatives being explored in Britain today are far too many and diverse for that. We have merely presented what we have found in the time we had at our disposal. For this reason we have given, in source guides at the end of each chapter, lists of contact points, addresses, books and periodicals which we have found helpful and which can be used to follow up particular points in greater depth.

In the television series we set out, as far as possible, to allow those we interviewed to present their own commentary on the activities we filmed. We have followed the same method in the book, which is why we have used so many extended quotations, many of them taken from the transcripts of the interviews we conducted for the programme. The idea was to let the Alternative Movement speak for itself.

Any television series, and any publication arising from it, is necessarily a team effort. This has certainly been the case with 'Alternatives'. So we should like to thank the film crew, the film editors and all our colleagues who participated. In particular we should thank HTV's head of education, David Alexander, for his encouragement throughout the project; Shân Hughes Davies, our production assistant, for keeping in order a potentially chaotic schedule; John Roberts, our film director, for keeping our feet very firmly on the ground; and our executive producer, Geraint Talfan Davies, for enabling the project to happen in the first place.

John Osmond and Angela Graham
July 1984

1

THE ALTERNATIVE MOVEMENT

People talk of the collapse of existing society. I hope that doesn't happen. I hope it slowly subsides over the next few hundred years and gradually transforms itself into another kind of society — a healthier one that doesn't damage the environment and the planet as much as the one we live in nowadays.

John Seymour

We began in a small way, with the idea of making a single half-hour television documentary about alternative forms of energy. We had come across a group of people in West Wales who had joined together to buy loft insulation material more cheaply. They then realized that each was exploring different ways of tapping renewable sources of energy to run their homes and businesses — using solar, wind and water power. So they decided to set up an Energy Group, the first of its kind in Britain though there were many in the United States, to promote their ideas and act as a pressure group on their local authority.

Many of these people had, for a variety of reasons, left secure jobs in cities in search of a more rural and a more self-reliant way of living. Most were short of money as a result. So the search for ways of reducing electricity bills was a prime motive in their alternative energy initiatives. But they also worried about the impact on the environment of the energy industry, particularly the nuclear industry, and saw their use of 'soft' renewable energy as a gesture, a signpost pointing society in the right direction.

After we met them we discovered that they were not the only ones involved in alternatives. There were many others. And they were doing much more besides harnessing the sun, wind and rivers. Some were worried about the long distances their children were travelling to large, impersonal schools. So they had set up their own. Most would not dream of consulting a general practitioner or attending a hospital, except with emergencies like a broken leg. Instead they sought the advice of a range of alternative therapists. One was a herbalist himself. All were involved to a large extent in growing their own food, much of it organically. One or two had tipis in their back gardens and lived in them during the summer to gain a greater affinity with the earth and the rhythm of the seasons. One we came across lived in his tipi all the year round. A few were engaged in more esoteric self-discovery pursuits like rebirthing: a continuous breathing technique that works on the principle that there is a direct connection between mental and physical well-being and the openness of breathing. Most appreciated the value of meditation. All of them knew each other and communicated using an informal system they called networking.

At about the same time we came across a book describing similar kinds of people, but in the United States. Called *The Aquarian Conspiracy: Personal and*

Previous page: *Networking is more than communicating for it entails action on the part of those involved. Pictured here is the first formal networking centre in Britain, with full-time and part-time staff outside the Greenhouse at Bangor, North Wales.*

Social Transformation in the 1980s, by Marilyn Ferguson, its opening paragraph read:

> A leaderless but powerful network is working to bring about radical change in the United States. Its members have broken with certain key elements of Western thought, and they may even have broken continuity with history. This network is the Aquarian Conspiracy. It is a conspiracy without a political doctrine. Without a manifesto. With conspirators who seek power

Satish Kumar helped to found the alternative secondary school we look at in Chapter 3. He and his wife are self-sufficient in food as far as possible and also edit 'Resurgence', a magazine dedicated to holistic living which is a forum for the Alternative Movement.

only to disperse it, and whose strategies are pragmatic, even scientific, but whose perspective sounds so mystical that they hesitate to discuss it. Activists asking different kinds of questions, challenging the establishment from within.

This appeared rather apocalyptic but it encouraged us to pursue our researches, and eventually the idea of producing a film about alternative energy grew into a series on alternatives embracing the whole of life. And indeed the idea of wholeness rapidly became central to the whole project. But rather than as a conspiracy we preferred to think of the alternative ideas and activities we were discovering as forming part of a movement. Both imply change, but conspiracy suggests a change of a revolutionary kind. The alternatives we were coming across were more about evolution or change from within.

Some of the people we spoke to when we were preparing this book and the television series it sprang from, questioned the title 'Alternatives'. They felt it placed too great a sense of distance between them and society at large. For those involved in the Alternative Movement do not feel there is any realistic alternative to the path they have chosen. If Society is to survive and develop a more civilized culture, they feel it will have to change gear and adopt a completely new set of values and, as a result, priorities. This is not to say that the Alternative Movement is an all-embracing credo or a manifesto for a new society. The essence of the movement is that it has no organization, no centre, no leader, and most of all, no dogmatic set of beliefs. Nevertheless, those within the Alternative Movement are instantly recognizable. They do share in common an approach to life and a set of values that make sensible the cohesive notion of a Movement.

For people within the Alternative Movement have abandoned views such as: rational thought will solve all problems; life is a competitive struggle; and unlimited progress will come through economic and technological growth. They have, perhaps most fundamentally, abandoned the directive given in Verse 28 of the first chapter of the Book of Genesis, a directive that still acts as a driving force behind much of contemporary society:

Be fruitful and multiply and replenish the Earth and subdue it, and have dominion over the fish of the sea and over the fowl of the air and over every thing that moveth upon the Earth.

Central to the thinking of the Alternative Movement is the belief that humanity's attempt to 'have dominion over' the world has led directly to the plethora of political and economic crises that regularly preoccupy the news media. Moreover, the dominating, essentially masculine, impulse behind Western culture's urge to *master* the environment explains the thrust towards centralization, uniformity, and the spiritually crippling alienation of mass, urbanized society. Certainly, this is the Alternative Movement's view of the world it has left. In its place it is endeavouring to promote an ecological holistic vision that gives emphasis to intuitive and emotional — essentially feminine — impulses as well as rational analysis; that emphasizes co-operation rather than competition; and that emphasizes environmental consciousness rather than economic growth. In place of the Old Testament directive quoted above it would sooner contemplate St Matthew's New Testament suggestion to:

> Consider the lilies of the field, how they grow. They toil not, neither do they spin; and yet I say unto you that even Solomon in all his glory was not arrayed like one of these.

The term 'holistic' used in conjunction with 'ecological' is central to the Alternative Movement's perspective and will recur time and again when we describe the Movement's activities. *Resurgence,* a magazine of the Alternative Movement, edited at Hartland in Devon by Satish Kumar and June Mitchell, is deeply concerned with holistic thinking. Founded in the 1960s by a group of people identified with Fritz Schumacher's ideas of appropriate technology and the small scale, it described itself during the 1970s as 'a voice of new civilization, a journal of new politics concerned with small nations, small communities, decentralization and ethnic cultures'. In the 1980s the balance in the magazine has swung towards discussion of more philosophical, ecological and spiritual issues as well. Satish Kumar was brought up from the age of nine by wandering Jain monks in India, and in the early 1960s 'walked the world for peace' through the world's nuclear capitals. He then worked for various international peace organizations and among the rural poor in India before ending up in London and taking over the editorship of *Resurgence.* He and his wife June and their two children took the magazine out of London, first to Wales and now Devon where they have helped found an alternative school, which we describe in Chapter 3, and also follow a self-sufficient lifestyle. Poised between two cultures, the East and West, Satish Kumar is well placed to explain the holistic approach:

> Our society is very much geared towards specialism. If you go to see a doctor he will see the particular symptom that you have a pain somewhere, or you have an ulcer, or a cancer, and he will treat that particular part. You go to an economist: he will analyse the problem in terms of economics and say his concern is not to think about moral, philosophical or political issues. You go

"YOU WHOSE DAY IT IS, MAKE IT BEAUTIFUL.
GET OUT YOUR RAINBOW COLOURS
SO IT WILL BE BEAUTIFUL."
                    NOOTKA INDIAN

THE EARTH IS 93 MILLION MILES
FROM THE SUN

EVEN IN NORTHERN
LATITUDES ALMOST ...   SOLAR ENERGY IS STEADILY
THE ANNUAL DOMESTIC HOT   AVAILABLE, WIDELY DISTRIBUTED,
WATER CAN BE SUPPLIED   INEXHAUSTIBLE, AND DOES NOT
BY THE SUN.   POLLUTE THE ENVIRONMENT.
                                        DR F.A. BACON

"WHEN YOU START EXPERIMENTING WITH
SOLAR HEATING BY COVERING COLLECTORS
WITH GLASS OR PLASTIC AND FEELING
THE WARM AIR BLOW OUT ...
WELL, IT'S SO EXCITING THAT ...
GET HOOKED AND CAN'T STOP ..."

"WE MADE SACRIFICES TO THE SUN,   THE CENTRE OF THE SUN
AND OUR PETITIONS WERE GRANTED."   IS ABOUT 20,000,000°F

ONLY A TINY FRACTION
OF THE SUNS ENERGY IS
CONVERTED BY EARTH INTO
ALL THE FOOD, TIMBER
AND OTHER VEGETATION
THAT GROWS ON EARTH,
AND ONLY A FURTHER
FRACTION OF THIS GROWTH
EVENTUALLY TURNS INTO
THE FOSSIL FUELS WE'VE
BEEN SQUANDERING
SO RECKLESSLY.

ALMOST ALL SPACECRAFT   "WE DANCE ROUND IN A RING AND SUPPOSE,
ARE POWERED BY THE SUN   BUT THE SECRET SITS IN THE MIDDLE AND KNOWS."
WITH SILICON SOLAR BATTERIES   ROBERT FROST

IN 10 DAYS WE RECEIVE
MORE ENERGY FROM THE SUN
THAN IS CONTAINED IN ALL
THE WORLDS FOSSIL FUEL RESERVES

GOD MADE TWO GREAT LIGHTS: SINCE THE ENERGY CRISIS IN 1973
THE GREATER LIGHT TO RULE THE DAY,   OVER 100 UK COMPANIES HAVE
AND THE LESSER LIGHT   BEGUN TO MARKET SOLAR COLLECTORS.
TO RULE THE NIGHT.
        GENESIS

                    THE SOURCE OF LIFE AND LIGHT,   SOLAR HOUSES ARE
"WHEN WE SEE THE CHANGES OF DAY   LETS LIVING SPRIGS OF WILLOW   BEING BUILT IN ALASKA,
AND NIGHT, THE SUN, MOON, AND   TELL OF SPRING;   AND SOLAR POWERED
STARS IN THE SKY, AND THE   TELL THE EARTH IS HALLOWED   REFRIGERATORS IN AFRICA.
CHANGING SEASONS UPON THE EARTH, BY THE GODDESS OF THE SUN
WITH THEIR RIPENING FRUITS, ANYONE THE SOURCE OF LIFE AND LIGHT.
MUST REALISE THAT IT IS THE WORK OF SOMEONE   TAPANESE POEM
MORE POWERFUL THAN MAN. GREATEST OF ALL
IS THE SUN, WITHOUT WHICH WE COULD NOT LIVE.

"WERE I TO CHOOSE A RELIGION,
I WOULD PROBABLY BECOME A WORSHIPPER
OF THE SUN. IT GIVES LIFE AND FERTILITY
TO ALL THINGS. IT IS THE TRUE GOD OF THE EARTH."
                              NAPOLEON I

"EVER THINK OF BUILDING A SOLAR ENERGY COLLECTOR
OR SUN OPERATED WATER HEATER, STOVE OR STILL?
HOW ABOUT A SOLAR TURBINE, STEAM ENGINE,
OR REFRIGERATOR? OR AN ELECTRIC CAR
WHICH HAS ITS BATTERIES RE-CHARGED BY THE SUN?"

to an educationist and he will also be a specialist. Now the Alternative philosophy is that all these issues are interrelated. You cannot, for instance, treat cancer on its own. You have to see what is the psyche of the person suffering from it, the way of life of that person, eating habits, how much sleep and rest. The same with farming. This is not just about producing food but also how that affects our relationship with the land. And it is the same with education and economics, with everything.

And, of course, once you start thinking this way it affects your whole life. You want to be a whole person. You don't just want to be an accountant, or a lawyer, or a nurse. You want to have some time for growing food, some time maybe in the kitchen, some time perhaps for producing a magazine. You want to do things that are intellectually satisfying, emotionally satisfying, and physically satisfying. This is the holistic lifestyle. People want to live this way because they have developed a holistic ecological philosophy.

Curiously enough the term 'holism' was devised by the South African statesman and philosopher General Jan Smuts to mean simply that the whole is greater than the sum of its parts. Smuts was strongly influenced in developing this idea by Ghandhi and, indeed, the holistic outlook is closely attuned to the spiritual philosophies of the East. But equally significantly, Western scientific thinking, and especially nuclear physics, has reached the same point, though by a different route. This convergence has been charted by the nuclear physicist Fritjof Capra in his book *The Turning Point,* which has become a sounding-board for the thinking of the Alternative Movement in the 1980s. Capra invites us to understand, and to participate in, a 'paradigm shift' — a transformation in the basic structure of our thought and understanding. In particular we have to take account of realities that are beyond rational thought: this is what both modern nuclear physics and Eastern mysticism teaches. The problem is, Capra explains, that our minds have become trapped by the scientific method promulgated by the seventeenth century philosopher Descartes. This is epitomized in his statement 'Cogito, ergo sum' — 'I think, therefore I am' — which has led to a split between mind and body, known as dualism. As Capra says:

> Retreating into our minds, we have forgotten how to 'think' with our bodies, how to use them as agents of knowing. In doing so we have also cut ourselves off from our natural environment and have forgotten how to commune and cooperate with its rich variety of living organisms.

This is not to say, of course, that Descartes' rational, analytic method of breaking down thoughts and problems into their component parts in order to

Opposite: *Wall mural pictured at the Future City Home, the Urban Centre for Appropriate Technology in Bristol. Many in the Alternative Movement, following the philosophy of the American Indians, regard the Earth as our Mother but the Sun as our Father.*

Below: *Fritjof Capra, a nuclear physicist who through his research at the frontier of atomic physics has reached conclusions similar to those of the Eastern mystics. An Austrian, Capra now lives and works in California.*

understand them has not made a major contribution. It is the foundation of modern science and ultimately made it possible, for instance, for NASA to put a man on the moon. But at the same time Descartes' view that mind and matter, spirit and body, are two separate and fundamentally different categories has led to major distortions:

> It has taught us to be aware of ourselves as isolated egos existing 'inside' our bodies; it has led us to set a higher value on mental than manual work; it has enable huge industries to sell products — especially to women — that would make us owners of the 'ideal body'; it has kept doctors from seriously considering the psychological dimensions of illness, and psychotherapists from dealing with their patients' bodies. In the life sciences, the Cartesian division has led to endless confusion about the relation between mind and brain, and in physics it made it extremely difficult for the founders of quantum theory to interpret their observations of atomic phenomena.

Holistic circle dance, the most visual expression of holism within the Alternative Movement. Colin Harrison, full-time dance instructor of Circle dance, says that by rediscovering these dances 'we rediscover something of ourselves: our roots, our source'.

Modern physics has had to cope with apparently incomprehensible things like particles that are created out of nothing, or go backwards in time, and the fact that the dichotomy between existence and non-existence is false one. Such problems make the link with mysticism. The main parallels between post-Einsteinian physics and Eastern philosophies, according to Capra, are

beliefs in: the interconnectedness of all things (including the observer and the observed); the unity of opposites; the unreality of space, time, and causality; and the continual dance of creation and destruction.

The term 'holistic' expresses the idea that systems act as wholes whilst still being parts of yet greater wholes. Every level of creation has two tendencies: an integrative tendency to function as part of a greater whole, and a self-assertive tendency to preserve its individual autonomy. How this concept is applied to humanity's relationship with the planet is something we shall explore morefully in the final chapter. Suffice it to say at this stage that the approach is critical for the Alternative Movement's ecological outlook and comes closest to providing its ideological foundation.

The most visual expression of holism within the Alternative Movement is the workshops promoting Circle Dance, sometimes called Sacred or Holistic Dance. As a dance form it is, in fact, among the oldest in European culture, but reintroduced into the late twentieth century it brings a refreshingly new approach. Colin Harrison, who gave up his job as a computer programmer to tour Greece and Yugoslavia discovering some of these dances and is now a full-time dance instructor, explained the significance:

> When we choose the first and simplest way of being together, we form a circle. Thus circles appear as a dance form in traditional cultures throughout the world, whenever people feel themselves to be one with the tribe or village. As the society changes, so the dance form changes, breaking the circle down into lines and crescents, eights and sixes, squares and couples, and finally into ones. Looking at the rock/disco scene of today, people dance by themselves, mostly unrelated to each other and without feeling themselves part of a whole.
>
> The oldest European dance forms are preserved in those countries on the fringe of our political and evolutionary events — such as Greece, the Balkans, Ireland, Poland. By rediscovering these dances, we rediscover something of ourselves: our roots, our source.

The Alternative Movement in the 1980s is very much about combining practical, often hard work, with an approach to life that remains idealistic. Nowhere is this more symbolized than in the efforts of those who have left the cities and settled in the countryside, usually on a smallholding. Place like Devon and Cornwall, west and north Wales, parts of northern England, and south-west Scotland — anywhere, in fact, where land is relatively cheap — are filling up with people seeking a more self-sufficient lifestyle. There has tended to be a rapid turnover in these people who often have not fully appreciated the hardships associated with living off the land and the fact that a cash income is still required. Whatever level of self-sufficiency is achieved, cash is still needed to pay off a mortgage, clothe children, pay electricity and phone bills, pay the vet when the goat gets sick, keep the battered Citroen CV — another symbol of the Alternative Movement — on the road.

In the 1960s and 1970s many people who moved enthusiastically to the land in pursuit of alternative values had not appreciated some of these hard realities, and fell by the wayside as a result. In the 1980s those people still pursuing the self-sufficient lifestyle have an air of the survivor about them. They have worked out a strategy for earning cash income, often by making craft goods to sell or providing a service needed in the community such as mending farming equipment, or finding a part-time job. A self-sufficient organic farming community we profile in Chapter 5 has developed a plumbing business, converting solid fuel heaters for central heating, as its major strategy for earning money. More than this, the 'back to the land' movement has now developed a number of 'schools' of self-sufficiency, where people who are thinking of changing their lifestyle can spend time to learn about husbandry and discover, relatively painlessly, whether it suits them. The most accessible is an organization called 'Working Weekends on Organic Farms' (WWOOF), an exchange scheme whereby bed and board are given in return for help in smallholdings, communities and organic farms throughout Britain. It was founded in 1971 by Sue Coppard, then a secretary working in London who decided she would like to get out into the country at weekends. Today it has a growing membership of more than 1,500 and a list of some 150 venues which reads like a inventory of the Alternative Movement. For instance, the entry in WWOOF's directory from Rob and Sue Lea, who live near Ellesmere in Salop, reads:

> Six-and-a-half acre family smallholding run on a part-time basis: quarter acre of vegetables, small orchard/soft fruit area, three-quarters acre woodland, house cow and two or three followers, chickens. Use compost, bonemeal, basic slag. Cheese, butter and yogurt making. Aims are to grow food and develop a balanced, sane lifestyle. Partial self-sufficiency — not fanatics! (Reasonable home brew produced.)

Elizabeth Robertson on the Isle of Tiree in Argyll wrote:

> Four acres with half-acre walled garden for vegetables and soft fruit. Cow, calf, sheep, 24 chickens, ducks, cats, dog. Some chemical fertilizer used on grazing land. Aim to produce organically the maximum amount of own food economically. Collect carrageen [edible seaweed] for sale and cooking. Sheepskin tanning, spinning, milking, hand-shearing, butter making. Elizabeth is an occuptional therapist and has a craft shop.

The way the WWOOF organization developed makes it a typical expression of the Alternative Movement. As the founder, Sue Coppard, now living on a smallholding in Wiltshire and supplementing her income by being town clerk with Bradford-on-Avon council, put it:

> One of the things I like most is that the organization is 'round-table' not pyramid shaped. It runs very well on joint consultation with no constitution or book of rules — which must prove something. This flexibility is a great advantage, given that by and large WWOOF attracts pretty good people (not many money-motivated ego-tripping drones are going to spend their weekends doing someone else's muck-shifting for the hell of it!). It began small and just keeps on developing where the opportunities lead. I suppose WWOOF's main strength is that its core is not theoretical, but practical activity. On top of that, it's fun.
>
> In my opinion, WWOOF has a very positive contribution to make in the difficult times ahead. Among the increasing number of unemployed in Britain's industrial conurbations there must be many who want to get out — or back — to the countryside and simply don't know how. WWOOF can provide practical help and opportunities for a life on the land. I have this theory that contact with nature is the psychological equivalent of vitamin C: without it we are deprived. We must find a way to reach those urban prisoners who want a greener, more 3-D life and are not yet into 'alternatives'.

For those seriously considering a change of lifestyle to live on the land, an appropriate introduction would be to spend time, a year if possible, on one of the smallholdings run as self-sufficiency training grounds by the Yarner Trust in the west of England. We visited one of them, Barton Farm at Welcombe in Devon. It is organized as a small community around the resident Rodway family, Nick and Pam and their three children. There is an extended community, too, with many other like-minded families and groups who have settled in the immediate neighbourhood. Many of them are involved in the running of the Small School in nearby Hartland which we profile in Chapter 3. Nick Rodway told us that rather than self-sufficiency, they prefer to talk more of self-reliance, understood as people taking more personal responsibility for their basic needs of food, clothing and shelter. Modern urban living has tended to make people lose touch with these basic attributes of life. Bringing people back into contact with the land restores a sense of wholeness to their lives and harmony with nature:

> It's a basic need, I think. Ever since people started leaving the land, long before the industrial revolution, there has been a constant stream of other people moving in the opposite direction. There do seem to have been times

when the movement has had more impetus, for instance at the start of World War I and just after World War II. There seems to be another spurt in the movement now in the 1980s.

This judgement appears to be borne out by migration statistics produced by the Office of Population Censuses and Surveys. These show that over the last twenty years there has been an increasing trend for people to move out of the cities into the countryside and, generally, from east Britain to west Britain. For instance in the ten years 1971 to 1981 the population of Greater London declined by three-quarters of a million to 6,805,200. In contrast the only areas of Britain that registered significant increases in population in the same period were East Anglia, Wales and south-west England. The personality most identified with the 'back to the land' movement, because of the many books he has written on the subject, is John Seymour. We put it to him that surely it was impractical to think in terms of thousands of people moving from the city into the countryside:

> I don't think you can talk about anything being practical for thousands of people, but for one person or one family if they really want to then there is nothing stopping them moving on to the land, growing some of the food they need, and finding some way of earning money.
> There is a criticism that too many on the land spoil it. But what spoils the land to me is too few people. I know vast areas in northern France, in Germany and in England where all you can see is an empty desert of wheat

John Seymour, perhaps the most famous spokesperson for the Alternative Movement, is pictured here above Fachongle Isaf, a 62-acre holding in Pembrokeshire which he ran as a school for self-sufficiency for many years. He has now divided the land up between his children who run it as a co-operative community. John Seymour himself now lives in Eire.

or barley. You can say this is productive because it's producing wheat or barley but, my God, it's not producing happy people. That's the crop I want to see — happy, contented, hard-working people.

I know a farmer in Cambridgeshire who farms 10,000 acres of land with three men to help him and a few contractors. To my mind this is a disastrous use of land. Alright, he grows a lot of wheat. But that's all he grows. He hasn't got a four-footed animal on the farm and as for people there's hardly anyone there at all. The local village has practically disappeared or been bought up by London or Cambridge commuters. No, the best crop a man can produce from the land is happy people and healthy children. That's what we should be doing.

The Alternative Movement has very clear views about the directions it wishes to take. They are in clear contrast to those pursued in the world it has left. One of the most concise statements of the difference between the two is contained in *The Sane Alternative: A Choice of Futures* by James Robertson, a former civil servant in the Cabinet Office who now acts as a management and

Left: Nick Rodway, resident warden of the Yarner Trust's Barton Farm at Welcombe, Devon. Bringing people back into contact with the land, he says, restores a sense of wholeness to their lives and harmony with nature.
Right: Pam Rodway with the children — Simon, Hannah (left) and Ruth (also Esme, their pet goat).

systems analysis consultant. He defines the choice of futures between what he calls HE and SHE alternatives. The HE — Hyper-expansionist — future holds that

> ... we can break out of our present problems by accelerating the super-industrial drives in Western Society, in particular by making more effective use of science and technology. Space colonization, nuclear power, computing and genetic engineering can enable us to overcome the limits of geography, energy, intelligence and biology. This view appeals to optimistic, energetic, ambitious, competitive people for whom economic and technical achievement is more significant than personal and social growth. They are often male. Their preferred future offers bigger toys and more important jobs for the boys.

On the other hand, the alternative SHE — Sane, Human, Ecological — future, holds that, instead of accelerating, we should change direction:

> The key to the future is not continuing expansion, but balance — balance within ourselves, balance between ourselves and other people, balance between people and nature. This is not a recipe for no-growth. But the crucial new frontiers for growth now are social and psychological, not technical and economic. The only realistic course is to give top priority to learning to live supportively with one another on our small and crowded planet. This will involve decentralization, not further centralization.

This alternative perspective has highly significant repercussions in the economic field, particularly so far as employment and unemployment are concerned. In June 1984 an alternative economic summit was organized in London to coincide with the 'conventional' summit hosted by the Prime Minister, Mrs Margaret Thatcher. Called 'The Other Economic Summit' it was attended by 140 men and women from 16 countries. The preamble to its final communiqué attacked the 'lack of vision' of the conventional summit meeting nearby: 'Despite their announced intention to address the issue of environmental degradation the underlying problems remain. The very nature of the large-scale mass industrial system — now dominant in all developed countries — has become economically and politically insupportable to people of the whole planet and to the planet itself'. At 'The Other Summit' James Robertson presented a paper asking 'What comes after full employment?':

> The possibility cannot now be ignored that employment may be becoming an uneconomic way of getting much important work done, just as slavery became uneconomic in its time. The realistic and responsible expectation

must now be, not only that many years of high unemployment lie ahead, but that full employment may never return again.

The answer, Robertson suggested, was to change towards a more decentralized society in which increasing numbers of people would organize useful and rewarding activity for themselves:

> Instead of a widening split between those who work and those who live lives of leisure, there will be a merging of work and leisure in many people's lives. Instead of a shift to a super-service society dominated by experts, there will be a shift to self-service and mutual aid; increasing numbers of people will take more control of their work and other aspects of their lives.

Networking

Not only does the Alternative Movement have a broad ideological approach to a whole sweep of issues, it has informal but highly effective systems for communicating and to some extent implementing the ideology as well. This is universally known in the Movement as 'Networking', which because it is a system for connecting like-minded committed people is more than merely communicating: for networking always entails action on the part of those involved in it. James Robertson, for instance, whose main interest is in developing new economic perspectives for the Alternative Movement, has established an international network of people with similar interests known as The Turning Point Network. Another highly influential international networking group is Ecoropa — the Europe Group for Ecological Action — which has a presence in ten European countries. In Britain it has a membership of about 500 who each covenant £10 a year. But beyond these it has a contact list of more than 10,000 committed people — committed in the sense that they will buy campaigning leaflets Ecoropa produces on issues ranging from nuclear power and nuclear weapons to food and health and cancer prevention. Each contact orders and pays for on average around 100 copies of each new leaflet produced. This means that when Ecoropa decides to spotlight an issue it can guarantee a leaflet distribution of more than a million.

But networking is generally a more intimate and personal affair than might be conveyed by the activities of Turning Point and Ecoropa. Scattered round Britain in most main population centres are alternative bookshops and information centres that provide accommodation, facilities and general meeting points for the Alternative Movement. The Greenhouse in Bangor, a three-storey converted shop and offices in the town centre, is probably more sophisticated than most but is an example of what can be done. It was founded in 1980 by a range of alternative groups — health therapists; the North Wales Naturalist

Trust; the Campaign for Nuclear Disarmament; and women's groups such as the Women's Enterprise Bureau, Women's Aid and Rape Crisis. Between them they manage to service a £14,000 mortgage on the property and have won funding from a variety of sources such as the Manpower Services Commission to pay several full-time staff. One of the more interesting projects organized by the Greenhouse is the promotion of a cycle path south from Bangor through Snowdonia. The eventual aim is to link up with similar schemes dotted between north and south Wales to create a cycle path running the length of the country.

The Alternative Movement in the 1980s

Despite all these constructive activities the Alternative Movement of the 1980s is still fighting the image that became attached to it in the 1960s. Phrases like 'drop out', 'hippy generation', 'flower power', or even 'the Good Life' are ones that come easily to mind when thinking of alternative lifestyles. And to some extent, because the Alternative Movement does have its origins in the 1960s, they are part of its identity. But the 1960s were very different, both economically and culturally, to the 1980s. In the 1960s Britain, and the world economy generally, were still feeling the ripples of the post-World War II economic expansion. The insecurity associated with the oil crisis, world recession and long-term unemployment of the 1970s had yet to break. By the 1980s the tone was quite different: less tolerant, tougher, and more rigorous. Even the visual impressions and sounds of the pop culture were harsher. The world, in one sense, had become more realistic and so too had the Alternative Movement. But the links with the 1960s were still there. Many of those active in the Movement in the 1980s experienced their formative years in the 1960s. Unlike many others of their generation who embraced alternative ideas at that time, they have not 'dropped back' into conventional society — but stayed with it and grown and matured as a result. Pete West, now living in a commune near Cardigan which we feature in Chapter 5, recalled the time when he was a student at University in the late 1960s:

> At that time a lot of people were dissatisfied with things like pollution, with the job prospects that were open to them, with the general economic system really, with capitalism. I was very confused when I left University, so I took two years off and went to India to look for something different. When I came back I decided that I wanted to live a different lifestyle, with people more, and that seemed to coincide with what a lot of other people were thinking at the time. We didn't want to be so materialistic. We wanted to put more human qualities into our lives. We were just not very impressed with the middle class family background we had been brought up with. Basically, we didn't want to continue in the way our parents and grandparents had.

What distinguishes the Alternative Movement in the 1980s is its more pragmatic, hard-headed approach, coupled with a firmer philosophical foundation grounded in ecological thinking. Interviewed by *Resurgence* magazine in 1982 to mark the launching of his book *The Turning Point,* Fritjof Capra observed:

> The movements which originated in the Sixties and Seventies are just about to float together and coalesce. . . In Europe the Marxist left has strong social concern, but does not have the ecological vision. The spiritual groups of the human potential movement often don't have the social vision. What I think we are going to see in the 1980s is a merging of these various movements. What it comes down to is the need to adopt an ecological perspective. This perspective should permeate all areas: economics, the way you lead your life, your nutrition, the way you take care of your health, what kind of technology you use and so on.

Scale

All these questions are intimately linked by the question of size and scale. Perhaps the most formative thinker in this regard, though many in the Alternative Movement will not be aware of him, is the Austrian economist and philosopher Leopold Kohr. His seminal work *The Breakdown of Nations* was first published in 1957, but it has taken a quarter of a century for it to begin to gain the recognition it deserves. Kohr, who taught for many years in the United States and Puerto Rico but who now commutes between the town of his upbringing, Salzburg, and the town foremost in his affection, Aberystwyth, has been a formative influence on many alternative thinkers and not least Fritz Schumacher. The slogan 'small is beautiful' has ensured that even those who have not read Schumacher's book have probably heard his name. But it is Kohr who was the source of the inspiration for the idea. His writing is immediately captivating since, in common with all great teachers, his mode of exposition is largely through images and analogies. Here is a typical example of his style:

> The real problem of our time is similar to the one besetting a mountain climber in the Himalayas. His heart aches, his lungs fail, his ears hurt, his eyes are blinded, his skin erupts, and yet no heart, lung, ear, eye, or skin specialist can help because there is nothing wrong with any of his organs or his skin. His sole trouble is that he is too high up in the air. He suffers from altitude disease. And the answer is not to call in specialists but bring him down to a lower level. Only if he feels any of his pains still at lower altitude does it make sense to call in a physician.
>   And so it is with the *social* diseases of out age. It is not poverty that is our problem. It is the *vast spread* of poverty. It is not unemployment but the

dimension of modern unemployment which is the scandal; not hunger but the terrifying *number* afflicted by it; not depression but its world-encircling *magnitude;* not war but the atomic *scale* of war. In other words, the real problem of our time is not material but dimensional. It is one of scale, one of proportions, one of size; not a problem of any particular system, ideology or leadership. And since the size, the scale of social complexity takes its dimension from the society it afflicts, it follows that the only way of coping with it is, in analogy with the altitude disease, to bring the size of the afflicted society down to proportions within which man with his limited stature can once again assume control over it.

This is not, of course, to claim that scaling down the units within which we organize ourselves to a manageable size will be a panacea for all our ills. For, as Leopold Kohr adds, even in a holistic, small-scale and ecologically-balanced community, a hundred out of a hundred people will continue to die. But it is to say, and this is the fundamental ecological principle, that we must first give attention to the size of any problem before hoping to find a solution.

The Alternative Movement is often accused of being introverted and so

Leopold Kohr, pictured overlooking the town foremost in his affection, Aberystwyth. A formative thinker of the Alternative Movement he believes the critical issue is size and scale. He is fond of quoting Theophrastus Parcelsus who said: 'Everything is poison; it all depends on the quantity.'

concerned with achieving a self-sufficient lifestyle that it has a selfish disregard for the wider society within which it, of necessity, has to exist. This may be true of parts of the Movement, but more generally we have found an anxious awareness of the need to communicate with conventional society — not to convert but to seek to change through example. Many feel that simply living out their beliefs is itself a contribution to changing the world. It is a case, more often than not, of actions speaking louder than words.

We did, however, come across a few examples of where people active in the Alternative Movement are deliberately seeking to influence conventional society. The most novel was a business management training centre in Anglesey, north Wales. Patronized by established companies like Sainsburys, Marconi, Shell and Rank Xerox, it mainly organizes outward bound exercises to give tired middle-management executives a short sharp shock. The aim is to concentrate their minds on leadership and decision-making. But when they get back to the centre after a day's mountain climbing, pot-holing, or canoeing they may take the opportunity of chatting to one of the course leaders, Tim Macartney, who lives in the gardens of the centre, in a tipi. His lifestyle reflects a philosophy we shall be exploring in Chapter 6, and the managers attending the training centre evidently find it intriguing to say the least. A revealing comment was made to us by the director of the management training centre at Cornelyn Manor, Barry Thorogood:

> What has surprised me is the numbers of managers who come here who are looking for something alternative in their life. They are 40 years old. Sometimes their marriages are at risk. They are spending a lot of time at work. They are half-way through their life and coming to a point where they are wondering what it is all about.

A more deliberate attempt by the Alternative Movement to influence the world with its ideas is to be found at the Centre for Alternative Technology at Machynlleth in mid Wales. This has on public display much of what the Alternative Movement is about: renewable energy technology such as windmills and solar panels; organic methods of growing crops; even the thirty staff who run the place organize themselves communally. Each year some 50,000 people visit the Centre. We asked its director, Peter Raine, how far he thought they were being influenced in a practical way:

> The major way, I think, relates to the massive unemployment Britain is experiencing at the moment. A lot of people made redundant receive a substantial sum of money as a result. Many of them get very depressed and

go away to just spend the money. But some get themselves together and think: OK, here I am at 40, I've got a few thousand pounds, what can I do? And many of them are actually organizing and registering as worker co-operatives — about three a week are being registered at the moment.

So that's people changing their lifestyles. And lots of people are getting fed up with living in big towns. Lots of people come here and say they're really concerned about pollution, about lead in petrol, about acid rain. So, yes, I think we're having an effect.

The tipi has become a symbol of the Alternative Movement. Certainly middle-managers attending the management training centre at Cornelyn Manor in Anglesey, North Wales, find this one intriguing.

The impact of the Alternative Movement can best be gauged by how far and how rapidly its activities are spreading. Perhaps the most visible in conventional society are the Natural Food and Health stores to be found on almost every main shopping street. The Movement's major single impact is probably the increasing take-up of the seventy alternative therapies available in Britain ranging, as we shall see in Chapter 4, from relatively well-known specialities like acupuncture and osteopathy to rolfing, a massage technique, and aromatherapy, a branch of herbalism.

We began our research, as we have said, with the idea of concentrating on alternative energy. But it quickly became clear that it would be impossible to confine our attention to just one subject. The people we met were not just making use of renewable energy sources and concerned with conservation to save money. Their activities could only be understood in terms of a completely different — an alternative — view of the world. For, ultimately, it is the thinking that underlies the varied and widespread activities of the Alternative Movement that will be the major axis around which the consciousness of conventional society will change. As Gerard Morgan-Grenville, founder of the Centre for Alternative Technology and director of Ecoropa, expressed it:

> The Alternative Movement is an amorphous scattering of disparate people, predominately middle-class, to whom a central ideal appeals. This idea is founded in a changed perspective of the place of individuals in the world. The concept of total individual responsibility for our impact on our surroundings is a view of such fundamental importance and such overwhelming simplicity that its advent must be regarded as a milestone in human evolution.
>
> Global ecological stability is the principal goal and the many social changes proposed are in support of this aim. Such stability can only be achieved within a global framework of peace. Alternative values depend on this paramount need. Ecological stability is seen as being not only the key to continuing life on earth, but equally as a key to human fulfilment, world-wide.

Gerard Morgan-Grenville, director of Ecoropa and founder of the Centre for Alternative Technology — 'Global ecological stability is the principal goal. . .'.

Source Guide

There is by now a great range of books dealing with all aspects of the Alternative Movement. Some of the outstanding ones we have mentioned in the text, in particular Fritjof Capra's *The Turning Point,* published by Fontana paperbacks. Capra's book contains an extended reading list. Marilyn Ferguson's *The Aquarian Conspiracy* was originally published in the United States in 1980, but is now available in Britain, published by Paladin.

Resurgence magazine, which appears bi-monthly, is essential reading for those wishing to keep in touch with the thinking of the Alternative Movement. Back issues of the magazine have been put together in book form, entitled *Time Running Out.* This and subscription details for the magazine itself are available from: Ford House, Hartland, Bideford, Devon. The Schumacher Society, which offers a book service, is also contactable at the same address.

Another relevant, monthly, magazine, is *The Ecologist,* based at 73 Molesworth Street, Wadebridge, Cornwall. *Greenline* magazine, 'part of the diverse but converging green movement', is the most stimulating of a range of publications now emanating from the CND/Ecology Party stable, available from 34 Cowley Road, Oxford. The Soil Association, 'founded to further the philosophy of inter-related wholeness, in respect of health and food in particular', publishes a quarterly magazine, available from The Soil Association, Walnut Tree Manor, Haughley, Stowmarket, Suffolk.

For more details about the Holistic Sacred Dance network in Britain send a stamped address envelope to Colin Harrison, 7 Victoria Buildings, Glastonbury, Somerset. A good introductory book on the subject is Marie Gabriele Wosien's *Sacred Dance,* published by Avon Publishers and Thames and Hudson.

The contact address for Working Weekends on Organic Farms (WWOOF) is 19 Bradford Road, Lewes, Sussex. For copies of its brochure send a stamped addressed envelope. WWOOF has also published a source guide of organic and alternative organizations in Britain as well as a directory of the farms and smallholdings that belong to it. A related organization is the 'City Farms' movement which has established organic smallholdings with an accent on animal husbandry in many British cities. They are designed as exhibition centres and so welcome visitors. For details write to The National Federation of City Farms, 66 Frazer Street, Bedminster, Bristol. The Yarner Trust, which was established in 1978 'to investigate and demonstrate low energy, small-scale food production and renewable energy', can be contacted at either of its two farms: Eric Clarke, Beacon Farm, Dartington, Totnes, South Devon; or Pam and Nick Rodway, Welcombe Barton, Welcombe, Bideford, North Devon.

John Seymour has written nearly a score of books on self-sufficiency and alternative lifestyles. Among his better known are *Self-Sufficiency* and *The Fat of the Land,* both written with Sally Seymour, and published by Faber; and *Getting it Together,* published by Michael Joseph. Copies of *The Sane Alternative* can be obtained from the author's address, which is also the contact point of 'The Turning Point Network': James Robertson, Spring Cottage, 9 New Road, Ironbridge, Shropshire. The set of papers presented to The Other Economic Summit (June 1984) can be obtained by sending £10 to its headquarters at 42 Warriner Gardens, London SW1.

Ecoropa. the European Group for Ecological Action, can be contacted in Britain at Henbant, Crickhowell, Powys. Membership is at present £10 per year but anyone can become involved in its scheme for purchasing and distributing its leaflets. Send a stamped addressed envelope for details. The Centre for Alternative Tehcnology is based at Llwyngwern Quarry, Machynlleth, Powys.

Various directories of the Alternative Movement have been published, including *Alternative England and Wales* and *Alternative London* — both available from Wildwood House, 29 King Street, London WC2. More recently *Alternative Wales* has been published by Cilgwyn Publications, Trefelin, Cilgwyn, Newport, Pembrokeshire.

LIVING
LIGHTLY

Right livelihood of course is an old concept, it means taking responsibility even in the way we choose our livelihood: living lightly on the earth; not taking more than our share of the earth's resources.

Jakob von Uexkull, founder of the Alternative Nobel Prize

Alternative energy is one of the foremost causes of the Alternative Movement. The petroleum shortages of the early 1970s showed how precarious was the foundation on which our comfortable Western society rested. We were forced to face up to the fact that natural energy resources would run out — perhaps by the first decades of the next century in the case of some fuels. Many people, faced with the consequences of continuing to exploit them irresponsibly, committed themselves to 'living lightly' on the environment. They sought to conserve what resources there were and to make use of renewable energy such as sun, wind and water as an alternative to non-renewable fossil fuels (coal, oil, gas) and nuclear power.

Not only were we pillaging the earth recklessly for fuels but we paid little heed to the effect that using those fuels was having on the environment. A mountain of evidence that we were poisoning the planet led to a crusade for greening it instead.

But the most emotive catalyst behind the alternative energy movement has been the threat of nuclear extinction. The campaign against nuclear weapons leads many people into concern about the environment and thence into an interest in alternative energy. The fact that the same technology is behind both nuclear power stations and nuclear weapons makes the connection.

The Alternative view is that our energy strategy has gone wrong because countries consider their needs in isolation, yet no country is 'an island, entire unto itself' — least of all where energy is concerned. One country depends on another for oil and other fuels. Misuse of energy in one region quickly has repercussions elsewhere — for instance, polluted air from Germany reaches remote parts of Scandinavia within three days. Above all, there is a huge imbalance in the energy consumed by the developed and underdeveloped worlds: the USA, for example, with 6 per cent of the world's population, consumes a third of all fossil fuels.

To deal with issues like these we have to regard the world as a whole, since no solution will work that is not conceived on a global scale. The ecological and moral questions underlying energy exploitation and use provide, in fact, perhaps the most profound affirmation of the holistic philosophy we explored in the opening chapter. From a holistic viewpoint we are the stewards rather than the masters of the earth's resources, and nowhere is this more graphically illustrated

Previous page: *Sabena Roberts, seen here with two of her children, lives in a house built by Chris Day. It has a turf roof — an old Scandinavian method of insulation — and is completely self-sufficient in terms of energy. Electricity is supplied by this windmill, which keeps batteries inside the house topped up.*

than in the harnessing of energy and especially nuclear energy. The planet is accustomed to being penetrated every day by radiation from the Sun. But we, through our exploitation of uranium — the source of nuclear power — have interfered with the processes of nature in a fundamental way. Those worried about the possible effects often make an analogy with Greek mythology. The demi-god Phaethon came to a nasty end when he stole the chariot of his divine father, the Sun. The chariot's steeds rebelled when they found that the reins had been taken over by a weak mortal's hands. They plunged out of control, and the world would have been burnt to cinders if Zeus had not saved it from destruction by summarily thunder-bolting the Sun's presumptuous usurper. For the Alternative Movement, the myth of Phaethon is an allegory of the risk to which humanity has exposed itself by playing with atomic energy.

But the problem with questioning the use of conventional energy in a country like Britain is simply that, for the time being at least, we do not have an energy problem. We are an island, the saying goes, built on coal — enough to last several hundred years — and surrounded by oil and natural gas. So what relevance have alternative renewable sources of energy? Leaving aside the exhaustion factor so far as fossil fuels are concerned, the answer lies in the weight given to environmental and ecological considerations. This is certainly the case with nuclear power, but it applies to the fossil fuels as well. Oil spillages pollute the seas and beaches, but worst of all is the damage done by burning coal. The gases emitted by coal-fired plants mix with oxygen and water vapour in the air and turn into sulphuric and nitric acids. Oil-fired plants, heavy industry and vehicle exhausts also contribute to this process. Eventually the acids fall in rain or snow, sometimes hundreds of miles away depending on the wind. Acid rain is destroying historic buildings like the Parthenon in Athens and the Taj Mahal. Up to 50 per cent of corrosion on cars may be caused by it. Plants and crops are destroyed. In the German Black Forest vast acreages of trees are dying — as much as 38 per cent. Fish perish in contaminated lakes.

Although governments are concerned about pollution and the inevitable end to fossil fuels, it was the oil crisis of the early 1970s that galvanized them into action. They did not want to risk anyone having a strangle-hold on supplies, so most of them have committed themselves to extensive home-based nuclear power projects. In the 1970s nuclear power was presented as an alternative that would provide cheap, safe and clean energy. In the event it has proved to be expensive, risky and polluting.

The Central Electricity Board maintains that nuclear power stations are about 20 per cent less costly than coal-fired ones. But doubts have been raised about this claim, because nuclear stations cost more to build and have to be run

Opposite: *This energy-saving house at the Centre for Alternative Technology, Machynlleth, has solar panels at the foot of the side wall, but, more interestingly, a system for utilising passive solar heating all the way up the wall as well.*

Below: *The Centre has a dozen types of windmill on display as part of its exhibition of energy-conscious techniques. Pictured here is a Climax multi-blade windmill used for pumping water on farms.*

at a lower output than was originally estimated. The cost of running a nuclear power station down at the end of its life and of long-term storage of radioactive waste could well be many times greater than building the station in the first place. Plutonium, which is one of the by-products of nuclear generation, remains active for half a million years — that is, one hundred times longer than recorded history. It would only take ten pounds of it, uniformly dispersed as dust amongst the world's population, to induce cancer in every person on earth. Britain produces this amount of plutonium every day — two tons in a year. Somehow this has to be stored — safely — somewhere. At present all the country's high-level radioactive waste is stored at the Windscale Nuclear Plant (now known as Sellafield for public relations reasons) while the government decides what to do with it. This promises to be the biggest stumbling block to the development of nuclear power as a replacement for dwindling stores of coal, oil and natural gas.

Before the early years of this century we simply did not have the capacity to do a great deal of damage to the environment. Even the idea that we could one day be capable of polluting an ocean seemed beyond the bounds of possibility. But population growth and industrial development mean that we are now pressing the environment too hard. A showpiece for the alternative — the choice of 'soft' energy — is the Centre for Alternative Technology near Machynlleth in mid-Wales. Gerard Morgan-Grenville, one of the founders, explained that by the early 1970s he had come to realize that many aspects of the average profit-orientated business concern were inevitably anti-environmental. It was essential to create an environment where the criteria for decision-making would be less commercial and more ecological.

The Centre, which opened in 1974, has examples from the main areas of alternative technology such as windmills, water turbines and solar technology. These are not only on display but are also integrated into the exhibition buildings: the lecture hall is heated by solar panels, for instance. There is an energy-conscious house which shows how the principles relate to an ordinary home. The whole complex depends on alternative technology. It generates its own electricity, is self-sufficient in food as far as possible, and recycles its waste.

The Newport and Nevern Energy Group

The Alternative Technology Centre is primarily an exercise in public relations, as we saw in Chapter 1. More relevant, from the point of view of demonstrating the viability of alternative 'soft' energy, is the Newport and Nevern Energy Group in Pembrokeshire. Its members use renewable energy sources to power their homes and businesses and have worked out collective cost-saving strategies

for energy conservation. Their chairman, Brian John, told us what led to the formation of the group:

Architect Chris Day, a keen member of the Newport and Nevern Energy Group, specializes in energy-conscious designs. His house was 'recycled' from stone of the original farmhouse and its shape is designed to blend in with the surrounding countryside.

It started with about a dozen friends, in 1980. We were all still quite concerned with the energy crisis. Costs of energy were rising and unemployment locally was high. We began thinking about the impact of high energy costs on the local community not just in terms of the amount that individual families were spending on energy but also on local employment structures and on local self-reliance. So we began to do a few sums and realized that every year something like a quarter of a million pounds was leaving our two parishes of Newport and Nevern to go for energy costs. You see we have no oil distributor in the community and no coal merchant. We thought, well, let's try and start an energy group; let's try to make energy conservation a local issue and keep at least some of this cash within the

community with hopefully all sorts of spin-offs in terms of local job opportunities.

The quarter of a million pounds was made up of fuel-bill payments of the 560 householders in the sparsely populated Newport and Nevern district. Even a 20 per cent reduction in energy demand would produce £50,000 that could be used to benefit the community. The group aimed to encourage efficient use of existing energy resources and energy-saving techniques and to promote small-scale power generation projects. They started by organizing bulk-purchase of loft insulation for group members which halves the cost. The District Council soon realized that this was helping its funds for insulation grants to go further. Three people have been employed with Manpower Service Commission funding to run an energy information centre, and the group has organized a national competition to encourage energy efficiency and conservation.

This West Wales initiative has inspired similar developments in other parts of Britain, although none of these has shown the staying power of the Newport and Nevern group. This may be because the energy issue has been overshadowed recently by the nuclear threat and many people have put their efforts into the anti-nuclear lobby. But Brian John feels that local energy efforts have a significance wider than just what they achieve in their own area:

> Although Britain seems to have plenty of coal, oil and other resources the government keeps on pushing nuclear power — and so does the nuclear construction industry. Energy prices are still rising very fast so no matter how much energy Britain has; as far as the individual householder is concerned costs are still going up and up at a very rapid rate.

By 1984 the Newport and Nevern Energy Group's membership had grown to an impressive two hundred. One of its most active members, Chris Day, is an architect, who has specialised in energy-conscious designs. He described how he put his ideas into practice when rebuilding the ruin of a small farmhouse he and his family moved into in 1978:

> The strategy I adopted was to make use of the two sources of free energy available on the site — water power from a stream and solar power from the sun — and co-ordinate them on a seasonal basis. The stream powers a small hydro-generator which supplies the house with electricity. Solar panels on the roof heat our water supplies. In winter, when there is less sun, the flood of water in the stream compensates and we are able to heat our water using electricity from the hydro-generator. In summer the power from that source reduces because there is less water in the stream. But then we have more sun so we are compensated by the extra output from our solar panels.

The house is attached to the mains electricity in case of emergency but in practice this is rarely used. In recent years the Days' electricity bill has not exceeded £3.50.

Solar energy can be used both as 'passive' and as 'active' heating. 'Passive' solar heating occurs when the building itself traps and stores heat; 'active' solar heating means using some kind of device to collect the sun's heat. Both forms are used by Chris Day.

Solar panels are the most common form of active heating and he has used them to roof the kitchen. A solar panel consists of a metal plate (usually copper, steel or aluminium) blackened in order to absorb as much heat as possible. Hollow tubes filled with water or anti-freeze are mounted on the back of the panel. The sun warms up the black plate which transfers this heat to the tubes and thence to the fluid. The fluid circulates between the solar collector and the storage tank, often with the help of a pump, which in many cases is activated by heat sensors and only works when there is useful heat to be collected. Most simple flat plate collectors deliver heat at about 50 degrees centigrade. More advanced designs can produce 90 degrees centigrade and really elaborate non-domestic ones can go as high as 300 degrees centigrade.

Passive solar heating plays a large role in keeping electricity bills low. Houses should be designed to get the maximum benefit from the sunlight. The room where the family spend most time during the day should be south-facing. Chris designed his house with these principles in mind. He built a greenhouse against one of the kitchen's walls. This traps and magnifies the heat of the day, and when the temperature falls in the evening the stonework radiates out the heat that has been stored up. Other features of design help make houses efficient. By placing the chimney at the centre of the house rather than on an exterior wall and grouping all the rooms around it at different levels, Chris Day exploits the heat that usually comes through the chimney walls which in most houses is lost into space. He used this technique at another of his houses, Ty Cwrdd Bach (Welsh for 'Little Meeting House'). This house has a turf roof which is a Scandinavian method of insulation and is completely self-sufficient in energy, obtaining its electricity from a windmill.

Another member of the Newport and Nevern Group meets the energy needs of his home and his wood-turning business mainly by farming his hedges. That is how Peter Bossom described the ancient technique of coppicing:

> The trunks of trees are cut close to the ground so that they sprout into slim branches which form the hedgerows. I crop these branches on a ten-year rotational basis, thinning out fifty yards of hedge in any one year. The timbers I prefer to use are willow and ash as they produce substantial

Brian John is shown here inspecting the solar panels on the roof of his house. He was the first person taken to court in Britain for witholding the percentage of his electricity bill that goes towards the nuclear programme.

quantities of wood very fast. Over the ten-year period of growth each fifty yards of hedgerow will produce enough timber to heat a three-bedroom house for a whole winter.

Coppicing is not as popular as it was because modern farming does away with hedges. But hedges actually reduce the amount of chemical fertilizer you need. The hedges round a twelve-acre field can provide three-fifths of domestic heating fuel.

Other kinds of natural energy sources are appropriate to farming as another member of the group, Wynford Evans, discovered when he installed an anaerobic digester on his dairy farm. This extracts methane gas from cow slurry. He explained how it works:

> The digester is a large, air-tight, concrete tank. I use a windmill to work a mechanical agitator within it which mixes the slurry and helps prevent a crust forming on the top. A heating source inside keeps the slurry at the necessary even temperature. The "bugs" that create the gas are present in the cow's digestive system and hence in the slurry. The device just provides the conditions in which the bacterial decomposition of the slurry is speeded up. The gas produced is mainly methane. I just pipe it off and into a specially converted domestic stove. We save about 1,000 gallons of oil a year which is worth between £800-£900. There is an agricultural benefit too: when the slurry has been through the process the fields can assimilate it more quickly and cows can go out to graze sooner.

David Meyrick capitalized on the windy situation of his farm by installing a windmill which heats his farmhouse:

> An alternator on the windmill produces electricity which is taken by cable to the house. There it is plumbed through an immersion heater into the domestic hot water system which also heats the radiators.

Another of the group's members runs his business on water power. Mike Hall is a miller and grinds his flour using a water wheel. Water from a small river collects in the mill pond and is channelled through a sluice to fall heavily into the scoop-shaped buckets fixed around the wheel's rim. The wheel is connected to a set of gears which in turn operate the millstones. Water wheels are suitable for this kind of direct generation of power, but do not reach speeds fast enough to produce electricity.

The Newport and Nevern Group is, of course, situated in a rural area which has a much wider range of alternative energy options open to it than an urban setting. Nevertheless, the principles on which the Group is founded have a

Peter Bossom belongs to the Newport and Nevern Energy Group and practises the age-old art of coppicing. A short length of coppiced hedge can heat a three-bedroom house for a year.

relevance for people living in towns and cities, though they would have to apply them in different ways, as Brian John explained:

> We see today that energy supplies are becoming increasingly centralized and that local communities have less and less control over their own destinies, especially if they happen to feel that living sensitively with the environment is important. Local self-reliance is crucial. It's more difficult to use renewable energy if you live in the middle of a city but there are many ways in which you can reduce your dependence on a centralized energy supply system. So some of the things that our group is doing in rural Wales are also valid for urban communities as well although their tactics would have to be slightly different.

The Future City Home
In the heart of Bristol is an exhibition of those tactics in an (ambitiously titled)

Far left: *Another member of the Newport and Nevern Energy Group runs a flour mill with the mechanical power supplied by this water wheel. Water power comes into its own as a generator of electricity in areas remote from power stations.*

Left: *Mike Hall checks newly-ground flour.*

Future City Home. Number 101, Philip Street is also called the Urban Centre for Appropriate Technology, and aims to demonstrate the relevance of energy-conscious technology to life in a city environment. It is a Victorian house that has been 'recycled', as the staff like to put it, by using the original materials in the renovation. It requires only one-third of the energy used in a conventional house. Hugh Barton, one of the staff, told us why:

> Our main energy-saving is achieved by conservation and by insulation of the walls, floor and roof combined with effective draught-proofing of windows and doors. As well as this we have a comprehensive system for recycling heat within the building. The end result is that we only need a boiler with an output equivalent to that of a four-bar electric fire. The majority of houses waste 75 per cent of their heat through the roof, 25 per cent through the walls and some via the windows and floors, not to mention other draughts. So it's obvious that insulation is absolutely essential.

In the Future City Home you can see in detail how a wide variety of insulation techniques work and also get ideas on how to exploit solar heat. There are a number of solar windows and the hot water supply comes from solar panels. The kitchen is particularly interesting. No energy is allowed to go to waste. For

instance, the oven's energy requirements are halved by heavy insulation; hot air from cooking is extracted and its heat is transferred to clean incoming air. Hugh Barton is convinced that alternative values can flourish in an urban setting:

> Think conservation! If all buildings were insulated to the kind of standards we recommend here, which are financially viable, then the amount of energy we would need in the form of oil, gas and electricity would be greatly reduced. We would find that instead of needing to build new nuclear power stations we would be spending less money and generating more jobs through conservation.

But how, in practical terms, do we achieve this kind of future, and is it the right kind of energy strategy for Britain? Members of the Energy Research Group at the Open University in Milton Keynes are looking for answers to these questions. But the funding behind such research is tiny compared to the amount spent by government on nuclear research and development. Dr Mark Barrett, a research fellow specializing in energy systems at the Open University, explained why:

> Political factors are most important of all in determining energy policy. Over the years we've seen the development of large and powerful coal, oil, gas and nuclear supply industries. These dominate the energy policy of the country and so the option of renewable sources is underplayed and underfunded. Even more significantly, conservation tends to be ignored even though it is a technically proven option. Conservation is certainly cost-effective in terms of the wider consequences of its use, for instance in reducing environmental damage. It should receive much more consideration and be a really important part of government energy policy.

We asked Professor Patrick O'Sullivan, a government energy adviser, why renewable energy sources do not get more attention. He replied that it was the government's first priority to ensure sources of supply:

> You have got to recognize that our main energy problem is low grade heat to keep our centralised urban society going. We do have a lot of energy available in fossil fuels which can provide the heat we need. Alternative energy sources merely channel energy into society via electricity. But electricity isn't our problem. The fact of the matter is that governments tend to look at their energy problems in shorter terms than they theoretically or idealistically should. The real choices that face the government this year are: should we spend more money on wind power or should we put more money into hospital beds? The fact is that with the superfluity of energy we have, for the foreseeable future there isn't the pressure to spend money on alternatives.

Left: The Urban Centre for Appropriate Technology at Bristol aims through its displays of energy-saving techniques to show how conservation is relevant to an urban environment. Among other features, a special solar window, seen here on the front of the house, maximizes the heating potential of the sun.

Inset: Insulation is the indispensable element of energy conservation in the home. Here a cross-section of a wall in the Centre shows how cavity wall insulation works.

41

Governments rarely look more than five years ahead, that is, beyond the future of the next election.

To the Alternative Movement, however, this is short-sighted in the extreme. For not only does the Movement look beyond the next election, but it looks into the next millenium — to the coming Solar Age.

The Solar Age

The American futurist Hazel Henderson has given perhaps the clearest exposition of the Solar Age. Our industrial society was built on fossil fuels and, in this century, on petroleum in particular. But the Petroleum Age and all it stands for in terms of competition and irresponsible egotism is drawing to a close. Solar energy, the Great Renewable, is the symbol of a new era which runs on a value system radically different from the prevailing one. Henderson maintains that we are moving towards the Solar Age through a transitional period that will entail not only major changes in technology but profound cultural shifts as well. Some of these we explore in the final chapter.

But how feasible is the application of Alternative Energy on a large scale? The major component must be solar power, and its potential is enormous. Already in Europe and the USA several solar power stations feed into the national grid. It is estimated that solar power could provide from 10 to 20 per cent of Britain's energy and possibly more. Hydro-electric power schemes, for instance, come into their own as suppliers of energy in areas remote from the central power stations, such as the North of Scotland. Tidal energy is not yet well developed in Britain, because of research costs. But it is being used successfully in France. The proposals to build a tidal barrage across the Severn Estuary indicate the possibilities.

About seventeen times the current world energy consumption is stored up in biomass. This is the term for organic material that acts as a storehouse for solar energy. Biomass, in the form of wood and animal dung, is the major source of fuel in the Third World. As we saw from Wynford Evans' anaerobic digestor, methane gas can be produced from biomass and refined biofuels are substitutes for fossil fuels. It is possible to run specially adapted cars on biofuel, for instance. The term 'biomass' also refers to refuse and other organic wastes. Liquid fuels can also be manufactured from these. This, along with a better exploitation of timber resources and efforts at timber conservation, is the best option for biomass in the context of large urban populations such as Britain's.

The consensus of energy experts sympathetic to the 'soft' options is that no single one of them is the answer to our energy question. But taken together with a sensible use of fossil fuels they could certainly meet our needs. 'Needs' is the operative word. The use of 'soft' energy first requires the recognition that consuming needlessly is ecologically counter-productive, and so far as nuclear energy is concerned quite possibly destructive of civilization as we know it. The idea of stewardship referred to at the opening of this chapter embraces the Alternative Movement's understanding of the intimate bond between energy and the environment, and also expresses humanity's role in relation to the planet. With stewardship goes responsibility, but also rewards. For the more we acknowledge our links with the environment and act on that recognition, the more we express our links with one another. But in the view of many in the Alternative Movement, the ultimate reward may be greater, even survival itself. As Gerard Morgan-Grenville put it:

> Alternative Technology provides the tools for communal self-sufficiency, without sacrificing comfort, without waste, without depleting non-renewable sources and without harming the environment. It is the means of saving the earth from ecological catastrophe.

Source Guide

Particularly helpful in preparing this chapter was *Solar Prospects: The Potential for Renewable Energy,* by Michael Flood of the Open University Energy Research Group (Wildwood House, 1983). Michael Flood was formerly Energy Consultant for the ecological group Friends of the Earth. His book provides a comprehensive survey of all forms of renewable energy. Though full of detail on technical processes, it is accessible to the general reader and offers a very good insight into the alternative energy situation in Britain and around the world. In conjunction with Robin Grove-White he has also published *Nuclear Prospects,* which examines the consequences of commitment to the nuclear programme. *The Schumacher Lectures,* edited by Satish Kumar (Abacus, 1980), gathers together talks from an annual series of lectures organized by the Schumacher Society, a body for promoting ecological ideals. This book contains contributions from the leading figures in the Alternative Energy field and covers both the practical and philosophical reasoning behind the choice of appropriate energy. Especially interesting are Amory Lovins on 'Soft Energy Paths' — a possible strategy for accomplishing the move towards a soft energy society; Hazel Henderson on 'The Coming of the Solar Age'; and the appendix by Leopold Kohr, the Austrian thinker to whom Schumacher was indebted for much of his 'Small is Beautiful' theory. In this section he sets out his ideas on the importance of appropriate scale in all things. This book is an excellent way into the thinking of the Alternative Movement on the question of energy in a wide context. Fritjof Capra's *The Turning Point: Science, Society and the Rising Culture* (Flamingo Books) is similarly useful in relating the energy issue to society as a whole, and has a detailed reading list.

Robert Todd, Technical Director at the Centre for Alternative Technology, has contributed a chapter on energy to *Future Conditional: Science, Technology and Society*

— a critical Christian View, published by the Methodist Church and available from the Centre at Llwyngern Quarry, Machynlleth, Powys. This book offers discussion points after each of the chapters, which cover, among other topics, Food and Farming; Arms Production; Electronics Technology; and Work, Wealth and Power. It contains enough detail, laid out in clear sections, to treat the subjects without becoming heavy, and its design would make it particularly useful for older secondary school students.

Details about how Britain could live practically on low energy are set out in Gerald Leach's *A Low Energy Strategy for the United Kingdom* (Available from 10 Percy Street, London, W1) and the Centre for Alternative Technology has published a booklet on the same subject, *An Alternative Energy Strategy for the UK*. The Centre also publishes leaflets which outline a range of energy topics. It is worth asking for their booklist as their bookshop specializes in alternatives in general. The ecological pressure group ECOROPA print leaflets in question and answer form on environmental issues, including nuclear energy. These are available from Nuclear Information, PO Box 11, Godalming, Surrey.

There are a number of organizations promoting alternative technology. NATTA — The Network for Alternative Technology and Technology Assessment — produces a bi-monthly newsletter and organizes annual national conferences. It can supply posters, speakers, a slide and speaker's notes set, an exhibition and an information file on *Community Action and Alternative Technology*. It also offers technical advice and careers advisory services. Its introductory publication is *Alternative Technology; an answer to the energy crisis?* The address is NATTA, Alternative Technology Group, Faculty of Technology, Open University, Milton Keynes, Bucks. It can supply a list of all the main British contacts for AT technical advice, courses, publications and pressure groups.

If you are thinking of following the example of the Newport and Nevern Energy Group, then the organization to contact for advice is Neighbourhood Energy Action, 2–4 Bigg Market, Newcastle upon Tyne, NE1 1UW.

There are several good guides to conservation in the home. The Urban Centre for Appropriate Technology, 101 Philip Street, Bedminster, Bristol, has a series of leaflets and can offer advice. The government Energy Efficiency Office has a booklet on the principles of home insulation and central heating controls called *Make the most of your heating* available free from the Energy Efficiency Office, Room 1312, Thames House South, Millbank, London, SW1P 3QJ. It also publishes *A guide to home heating costs* on a regional basis. You can apply to your local council for a grant to install loft insulation.

A comprehensive *Directory of UK Suppliers and Supplies in Renewable Energy* is available from The Solar Energy Information Office, Solar Energy Unit, University College, Cardiff. The Open University's *Keeping Warm for Half the Cost* by Phil Townsend and John Colesby (Prism Press) deals with domestic insulation problems, and the O.U. also publishes an excellent pack called *Energy Matters,* which, along with a large well-illustrated booklet, contains a questionnaire on your domestic energy consumption which the O.U's computer will analyse. It costs approximately £10 from the Open University, Milton Keynes, Bucks.

The Friends of the Earth Guide to Pollution (Temple Smith) is a useful introduction to this topic, and contains a list of books, magazines and organizations dealing with environmental matters.

DECENTRALIZING
EDUCATION

Previous page: Music is a vitally important part of the Steiner curriculum. Here Nant-y-Cwm children practise recorder playing with their teacher Betty Henderson.

Below: A few years ago this 'alternative' school was a derelict former primary school which had been empty for 20 years. Now it has been lovingly renovated by parents, working in their spare time.

Here you can have a laugh and a joke, and so long as you don't go too far it's OK. The school atmosphere is good, it helps you work a lot. It's like home, really, one big family rather than a classroom of kids all chucked together. I think because of the size — so far only fifteen pupils — and because you're all different ages there is more give and take. You work because you want to, not because you're being threatened with detention or anything like that.

A comment such as this one from fourteen-year-old Patrick, a pupil at The Small School in Hartland, Devon, is perhaps the best place to start in any consideration of alternative education. What happens to the children is, after all, the major consideration. But the story of the two schools highlighted in this chapter is very much one of the enterprise, determination and often sacrifice of the parents.

Though prompted by different circumstances and different educational philosophies, both groups of parents shared a distrust of what was on offer from the State system. They disliked the large size and accompanying impersonality of the State schools. They were worried, too, about the emphasis on achievement that the conventional system is forced into by the pressure of examinations.

Moreover, they were concerned that the State system was less bothered about producing well-balanced personalities than children who would slot easily into a predetermined role, whether it be a University place, a secretarial course, or an apprenticeship. No-one involved in alternative education would declare that such objectives were unimportant; but they would all agree that, by themselves, they are too narrow, not least when the most appropriate question many fifteen-year-olds can ask their parents or teachers today is, 'What shall I do when I'm unemployed?'

The parents were prompted, too, by feelings that are more difficult to express. Put most simply, they shared the common view that, by merely handing over children for so many hours a week to a school world completely divorced from the home, they were abdicating their responsibilities as parents. They wanted to be more involved, not in a dominating way but in an integrated sense with the education of their children. Some parents take this view to the extreme of educating their children themselves at home, which is perhaps the ultimate alternative in education. But most of the parents we shall be looking at have adopted a less ambitious, though still demanding, option of setting up their own schools that accord more closely with their aspirations than those on offer from their Education Authority.

Nant-y-Cwm

Pembrokeshire in west Wales is, as we have seen in the previous chapters, a fertile area for the Alternative Movement, so it is not surprising that it is the home of one of the most thriving voluntary education initiatives in Britain: the Nant-y-Cwm Rudolf Steiner school at Rhydwilym, about ten miles north-east of Haverfordwest. Rudolf Steiner, an Austrian philosopher and scientist who lived between 1861 and 1925, developed a wide range of ideas that have been taken up throughout the Alternative Movement, not just in education. Though he was always concerned with the practical application of his ideas, whether in farming, medicine, science or education, the distinctiveness of his approach lies in his overall vision of the person as a spiritual being.

There are currently more than 200 Steiner Schools throughout the world, 15 of them in Britain, and in many places they are hardly viewed as 'alternative' at all; but in Britain, unlike other European countries, they receive no State aid. Moreover, they represent a distinctive philosophical approach to education that is foreign to the essentially·empirical and pragmatic attitude of mainstream British education. So in this sense it is fair to describe Steiner schools as 'Alternative' in the British context, particularly as the Steiner system embodies much of the holistic outlook that is common to the Alternative Movement.

Parents provide the main impetus for the founding and sustaining of alternative schools. A few are seen here collecting their children at the end of a day from the Nant-y-Cwm Steiner school in west Wales.

In north Pembrokeshire in the mid-1970's a group of parents interested in the Steiner approach came together first of all to start a Saturday playgroup for their children. This rapidly grew to 28 children, too unwieldly a gathering to meet in the homes of the parents. Then, in 1977, one of them came across an old school house in Rhydwilym that had been empty for 20 years and was now up for sale. Another of the parents, Chris Day, an architect, recalled:

> I said that we had no money, no teachers and no organization. It might be the right place, but it was definitely the wrong time. It was quite out of the question. Nonetheless, a group of us arranged to see the place. I remember it was a grey November day and raining. The place looked daunting. There were holes in the roof, broken windows, basically it was a ruin. But we decided to buy it. The price, £6,500, was loaned by members of the group. It seemed ridiculous at the time but in retrospect it is clear that it was meant to be.

With £36 in hand from the Playgroup finances the parents set about renovating the school. They raised another £40 from a barn dance and slowly the money began to come in. One day they arrived at the school to find a £1 note pushed under the door. An Autumn fair raised £500. Over seven years events, raffles and donations raised some £16,500, which, together with the voluntary labour of parents, created a school of a very rare quality indeed. Building is still in progress and takes place every Thursday during term time, with enough work for any parent who cares to turn up. By mid-1984 the parents had built four classrooms and a toilet block, and laid on all the main services, including water, electricity and drainage. At that stage the school housed 40 children, aged four to fourteen. The hope was to develop the school to full secondary level, so there was plenty of scope for further building work.

The running costs of the school pose different problems. In 1983, with three full-time teachers, the turnover was in the region of £18,000. This meant that each parent had to find £380 a year for each child, or £7.30 a week. There are no fixed contributions, however. The rule is that parents pay what they feel they can afford, many undertaking their own fund-raising initiatives, such as running weekly market stalls, to find the money. The average contribution per child in 1983 was £4 a week, with the remaining £3.30 (about £10,000 overall for the year) coming from collective fund-raising. Popular events are school fairs, and monthly 'school dinners' attended by parents and friends.

Nant-y-Cwm is far from being a typical 'private' school. The parents are not well off. Many are single parents and most are struggling to make ends meet, living alternative lifestyles, often off the land. Perhaps the most impressive aspect of the school has been its survival as a thriving, growing concern, since it opened in September 1979. As Chris Day put it:

> Our problems are by no means behind us. Building to provide more classrooms and to finish the unfinished continues, as does the financial strain of running and building the school. But when I look back it is extraordinary what has been achieved. The school is now a living organism, no longer vulnerable and dependent on a handful of individuals. No longer is it a building site and a dream. It is now a spiritual enterprise and a corporeal home.

The Small School, Hartland

The Small School at Hartland, a small village with a population of 1,300 near the north Devon coast, has very different roots to the Steiner school a Rhydwilym, but it shares in common an inspiring commitment from the parents. In the case of The Small School the commitment also has its source in the far-flung readership of the magazine *Resurgence*.

As we saw in the opening chapter, *Resurgence* is a magazine in whose columns the three main strands of the Alternative Movement — ecological, political and spiritual — come together. Since 1979 the magazine has been based at Hartland, where the editor, Satish Kumar, and the Managing Editor, June Mitchell, have their home together with their two children, Mukti and Maia. Founded in the late 1960s, the magazine rapidly became associated with the 'Small is Beautiful' ideas of Leopold Kohr and Fritz Schumacher and the 'Back

The Small School emblazons its name proudly above the door of the former Methodist Sunday School that is its home near the centre of the small village of Hartland. In the foreground is headmaster Colin Hodgetts.

to the Land' self-sufficiency philosophy of John Seymour. When he became editor in 1973 Satish Kumar added a spiritual, holistic dimension that drew on his Indian background: he had been brought up in the sub-continent by the Jain sect of wandering monks (see Chapter 1).

Taken together, these elements laid the foundation for the magazine's progress during the rest of the decade. But by the early 1980s the theoretical discussion and debate of these ideas was becoming divorced from practical expression. In the mid-1970s the magazine had already taken the practical step of moving out of London (in the footsteps of *The Ecologist* magazine), first to west Wales and then to Devon. In both places the editorial team practised smallholding self-sufficiency. Then when Fritz Schumacher died in 1977 the magazine became the focus for the formation of the Schumacher Society, which every year sponsors a series of lectures. Towards the end of 1981 Satish and June toured India where they were impressed by groups of people engaged in village and community work, especially in education. So when they returned to Hartland and discovered that the village's Methodist Sunday School was up for auction the germ of an idea began to take shape. As Satish recalled, the auction was to be held on 16 February 1982:

> If ever we were to put our idea of starting a village school into practice this was the time. We went to see the building. Two large halls, a small room, a garden, toilets and adjacent to it a two-bedroomed cottage, to be auctioned as one lot.
>
> Ideas started to explode. Discussion got going. Starting a primary school was out of the question because there was already a primary school in Hartland. The need was for a secondary school as children have to bus 15 miles to the nearest crowded 1,800 pupil comprehensive in Bideford.

At the packed auction in Bideford, made up mainly of people from Hartland, Satish, with no money even for a deposit, found himself bidding against a local builder and became, at a cost of £20,000, the owner of the property. *Resurgence* magazine made a temporary loan of the £2,000 deposit and the next issue launched an appeal for ten shareholders to invest £2,000 each. Eleven responded, so there was an extra £2,000 to start carrying out basic repairs. The school became the responsibility of the Environmental Research Association, a registered charity (by mid-1984 steps were being taken to register the School as a charity in its own right, with a constitution and governing body).

The next task was to find a teacher and the post was advertised. Although applications came in from all over the country the right person was found in Hartland itself: Michael Nix, a former teacher at the village's primary school who had given up his job to start a museum at Hartland Quay, a neighbouring community on the coast. He had lived in Hartland for eleven years and knew the local population well. As Satish Kumar put it, 'For a small school which is set up to focus on the community and the village, who could be a better teacher than him?'

The school opened in September 1982 with just nine pupils. A year later their number had grown to fifteen. By then the school had a new head teacher, Colin Hodgetts, a trained teacher and Anglican priest who had previously been involved in establishing a school for Vietnamese refugee children in Yorkshire. By September 1984 the school roll had risen to twenty-one, with an eventual target of around forty. The annual school fees are £600 per pupil, and it is estimated that when the school has thirty-six children it will be more cost-effective to run than local authority secondary education.

Although the fees are set at £600, the estimated break-even requirement, most of the parents pay considerably less. So far the balance has been made up by donations from charities and individuals. In its first two years the project raised more than £60,000. Much of this was spent on the launch costs; for instance, £5,000 was needed to buy books, stationery and equipment before the school opened. The remainder is being used to cover the running costs until the school builds up enough pupils to be self-supporting.

From the start there have been broadly two groups of children at the school: older ones whose parents had withdrawn them from the comprehensive school, fifteen miles away in Bideford, and a younger group whose parents sent them to Hartland for the more positive reason that they were anxious to take advantage of a different approach to education. The parents of the former group tended to be long-established inhabitants of the area, while those of the latter tended to have parents who had moved in and were generally themselves following alternative lifestyles. Balancing the different interests and expectations of these two groups of children and their parents has proved one of the most challenging problems of the school's early years.

Nevertheless, involvement of parents in the running of the school is a crucial part of the experiment. Once a month all the parents gather to discuss with the head teacher the school's progress, curriculum, fund-raising and social events. Parental integration goes much further than this, however, since a number of them actually teach some specialized subjects in the school's curriculum — for instance, French, physics and agricultural sciences. In addition, members of the local community who are not parents participate. The local doctor teachers biology one afternoon a week, and a local potter comes in for half a day to teach pottery. The holistic integration of parents, teachers and

Gardening is an important part of the curriculum at the Nant-y-Cwm school. Nursery-age children learn mainly by doing according to Rudolf Steiner's philosophy.

children in the context of a small, intimate school is seen as the most important aspect of the project. As Satish Kumar, who himself teaches comparative religion, put it:

> When a school is small the relationship between teachers, parents and children is much more important than the books and facilities. We want to create a model to show that small schools using all the resources of their local community can provide both better and cheaper education.

Steiner Education

While the main inspiration behind The Small School is to set an example for decentralized community initiatives in education, the Nant-Y-Cwm Steiner school set out to put into practice a more formal and systematized alternative curriculum. Its educational theory is built on the conviction that each pupil is the bearer of an evolving human spirit with a past and a future leading beyond birth and death. Steiner saw growing up to be the gradual incarnation of the individual human spirit into a physical organism and education to be an essential support to this process. Although this will appear to many as savouring too much of mysticism and the occult, the practical application of the theory now looks remarkably far-sighted in the light of the work done on child development since Steiner's time.

It is characteristic that Steiner emphasized the physical development of the child as much as the psychological. This accounts for the importance he placed on chronological age, as opposed to developmental age, and his stress on the importance of taking into account the connection between physical, emotional and intellectual development. All should be seen as a whole: intellectual development, for example, should not be allowed to proceed ahead of physcial or emotional development. If this happens it can lead to problems in later life.

Children, said Steiner, do not grow up — they 'grow down', from head to limbs. And as they grow down physically, they wake up psychologically, from limbs to head. The new-born baby is all head; the limbs are more or less appendages. The adolescent, by contrast, often goes through a stage when he seems to be all limbs, before reaching final adult proportions.

Babies and nursery-age children learn mainly by doing. It is the environment that most deeply affects them. The priority at this stage is to instil a sense of belonging in a secure and stable world that will set the foundations of the child's inner security.

The all-important phase of development, from Steiner's point of view, is the middle years — roughly between six and fourteen — which he placed explicitly between two stages of physical maturation: change of teeth and puberty. In this period the rhythms of pulse and breathing begin to approach the adult's, movements become more rhythmic and graceful, and the child is for a while beautifully balanced, until the awkwardness of adolescence begins. At the same time, a rich inner life of imagination, fantasy and feeling begin to unfold: everything becomes heartfelt. Only now, in the Lower School, do the children learn to write and read (in that order, to allow reading to grow out of physical appreciation of the shapes and sounds of letters and words). But still there is great emphasis on story-telling and music-making. The primary purpose during these years is to nurture the children's imagination and sense of beauty. The recounting of ancient mythologies often serves to blend English and history lessons into one. The year is a round of colourful and moving festivals, with each term's work given an orientation by the Christmas, Easter and the midsummer Solstice.

Throughout the eight years of Lower School a class remains with the same teacher. This ensures continuity, a close relationship, and, above all, establishes a natural authority which, Steiner said, children of this age instinctively look for: an authority that derives its strength not from any hierarchy, but from the enthusiasm and vigour the teacher expresses. The place of authority is, in Steiner's view, a critical aspect of child development. The small child is essentially imitative, and is supported primarily by security and routine. The adolescent is essentially critical, and is best guided on the one hand by reason and on the other by integrity. But in the middle years, the child expects and needs authority, a chance to place confidence in an adult as a source of wisdom and guidance.

The Steiner Curriculum

Steiner's suggestions for a school curriculum were both practical and detailed. With the younger children he urged teachers wherever possible to proceed from the whole to the part, from the living to the non-living, from action to knowledge, from man to nature. Thus, as already stated, writing precedes reading in Steiner schools, and writing itself emerges out of imaginative experience and action. So, for example, before introducing the letter W, the teacher may tell a sea story full of wind and waves. The children will act waves; learn a watery, wavy poem; and paint waves. Out of the painting the teacher will lead into the formal exercise of the letter form — an abstraction, but one born out of a living experience. The child thus follows, essentially, the same process as the historical development of writing, from pictograms to our present skeletal but convenient alphabet.

Throughout the first school years the children's imaginative life and grasp of language is nourished by hearing, retelling, acting and illustrating stories. For the six-year-olds the teacher may draw mainly on fairy stories, moving on to fables and legends at seven, to Old Testament stories at eight, Norse stories and sagas at nine, Greek myths and legends at ten. In using a sequence of this kind the teacher leads children gradually 'down to earth' through different qualities of imaginative experience, thus preparing the way for history proper.

It is generally recognized that the first experiences of arithmetic are crucial, and here Steiner made some interesting recommendations. By starting with 'two plus two equals four', the child meets (i) a completely abstract proposition; (ii) a

Throughout the early years of schooling great emphasis is put on the telling and re-enacting of stories and fables. Here some of the Nant-y-Cwm children rehearse a play they will present to their parents at the school's open day.

reductionist view of the universe in which wholes are made up of parts; and (iii) a problem with only one answer. If the child explores instead how to divide an apple or a cake and share it around the classroom, a start is made from real life, from a problem with several answers, and, moreover, from a perspective of wholeness. Although Steiner did not specifically articulate the idea, his view of the world was a holistic one and very much in tune with the broad thrust of thinking behind the Alternative Movement of today.

The Steiner way into science also follows a gradual path from imagination to observation and abstraction. For six-year-olds it seems perfectly natural for animals, plants and rocks to talk to each other, as well as to humans. By the ninth year, however, there comes an important transition on which Steiner placed much stress. One symptom is moments of sudden private loneliness and feelings of detachment from parents and home, often coupled with sudden rebellion. It can be like a premature glimpse of adolescence. To deal with this crisis the child needs to become at home with the world in a new way. Steiner suggested that children in this phase should come to know various forms of human work in which craft, skill and knowledge of materials and the environment are important. The children may churn butter, build a wall, help a farmer at harvest time, or learn gardening, which is a key aspect of Steiner education.

As puberty approaches, the physical sciences are first introduced more formally. Steiner anticipated a good deal of modern thinking about science teaching in recommending that a strong element of observation and discovery should precede theoretical explanation. But he also urged, perhaps less fashionably, that the artistic experience of earlier classes should not be banished from the laboratory. Thus Steiner teachers may begin physics with acoustics, which can be introduced through music, the making and tuning of bamboo pipes, and the playing of recorders.

The last four years of Steiner schooling, from fourteen to eighteen, are the time when the pupil becomes capable of more abstract intellectual activity, of the development of critical and analytical faculties, and the weighing of judgements. If all Steiner's stipulations concerning the development and curriculum of children at earlier ages are correct, the adolescent struggling towards maturity will benefit most. Thus the imitative needs of the infant, if not appropriately met, can re-emerge at puberty and make the adolescent hopelessly vulnerable to every passing fashion. And the natural need of the first school years to look up to some adults with affection and confidence as trustworthy authorities, if not adequately fulfilled, can manifest in the adolescent as over-dependence or indiscriminate worship of cult heroes.

Steiner died in 1925 and his educational ideas did not begin to be put into practice until 1920, at the Waldorf-Astoria cigarette factory school in Stuttgart (hence Steiner schools are sometimes referred to as Waldorf schools). Since then the world has moved on, and conditions for secondary level teaching in particular are very different. Steiner schools themselves, at this level especially, have evolved new approaches, notably in attempts to combine continued liberal studies and artistic work with industrial apprenticeships and various forms of craft and vocational training.

It is perhaps in this last respect that, though coming from very different inspirational sources, the Steiner approach has most in common with the curriculum development at The Small School in Hartland. Here there is a continual search for a balance between academic and practical subjects, to find what each individual child is interested in and to discover how real practical skills, as well as theoretical understanding, can be imparted. Thus prominent subjects on the curriculum are carpentry and car maintenance, weaving and pottery, typing and cheese-making, horticulture and cooking, as well as the more conventional academic subjects such as mathematics, physics and French. Parents, teachers and children are facing up to the reality that probably most children are not suited to an academic career, and that, equally important, most will want to remain in rural north Devon and will need an appropriate combination of skills and attributes to enable them to do so. With unemployment amongst young people so high, The Small School is taking on board the need to help each individual work out a strategy for economic survival in the harsh world beyond formal schooling.

Discipline and Responsibility at The Small School

Examinations are not a priority at The Small School. Where a child has aptitude and real motivation he or she will be encouraged to take 'O' and 'A' levels, but the philosophy at the School is not to make its routine or curriculum revolve around the demands made by examinations. As the head teacher, Colin Hodgetts, put it:

> I think that, by and large, the parents of our children are not saying that we should not put children in for examinations, but that everything should not revolve around them. They are seeking an alternative to the conventional secondary school situation where everything is geared up to doing exams. A lot of them are worried about the lack of moral and spiritual content in education. Parents have said to me that they want their children to behave and be responsible citizens and to have some substance to them as people. These are difficult things to achieve without long contact with children. In a big comprehensive you may see a child maybe two or three times a week,

Children at the Small School are encouraged to work out their own time-table for lessons. Here some are seen with founder and parent Satish Kumar (left) who teaches comparative religion, and headmaster Colin Hodgetts.

maybe for one year of their career. But developing the human being demands long term contact with and knowledge of your children. This alone militates in favour of the small school. Another thing the parents — all of them — have said to me is that, first and foremost, they want their children to be happy in school. That means that a very important task for me, perhaps the first task, is to provide a happy, cheerful, environment.

The most immediate consequence of this set of priorities is The Small School's attitude to discipline. The ultimate deterrent employed is simply to send home children who transgress beyond reasonable limits. During the first two years this only happened on two occasions. The idea the punishment is

intended to convey is that being at school is a privilege that can be withdrawn.

A different but connected theme arising out of the school's philosophy is to encourage the children to take as much responsibility as possible for devising their own timetable and projects. That said, there is a pattern to each day in the school which begins with a small assembly at nine o'clock. The children sit in a circle and sing a song or hymn accompanied by Colin on the guitar. The song is followed by a reading or a poem, usually written for adults but carefully chosen and explained in order to stretch the children's imagination. There is then a short period of silence, perhaps lasting three minutes, sometimes a little longer. At the outset this proved difficult for the children, who often broke into uncontrollable giggling. But gradually they became used to the idea, which has more than proved its worth, since good concentrated study usually follows such a period. But there is more to it than that. It symbolizes another part of what the Small School is trying to achieve: to make the children aware of a stillness at the centre of themselves, and to break the pressure of constant striving for attention, and competition.

A Day at Hartland

Mornings at Hartland are taken up mainly with academic subjects — mathematics, English, geography, human biology, physics, French, typing, history and agriculture. These are taught by outside volunteers, among them parents, as well as the headmaster and his full-time assistant, Maggie Agg, a marine biologist who joined the school in September 1984. In addition the school has the invaluable service of a full-time man and wife team, Chris and Becky Howe, who act as caretakers as well as participating in some teaching and the general running of the school. They live in a cottage that is an integral part of the school buildings and their twin daughters attend the school as well.

During the morning, two of the chidren, working to a rota, help in the preparation of lunch, invariably vegetarian and wholefood, and learn about nutrition in the process. Lunches are not vegetarian in principle but because they are cheaper, because most people eat far too much meat, and because some of the children are vegetarian at home. Experience has shown that two children can provide lunch for between sixteen and twenty people virtually without supervision. Some of the food is grown in the school's own gardens worked by the children.

Afternoons at the school are usually taken up with project work, basketmaking, pottery, painting, drawing, gardening, music, maintenance work, technical drawing and games. At this stage in the day the children have dispersed throughout the building and outside to concentrate individually on

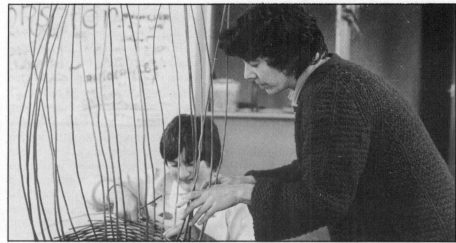

The Small School relies on parents and others with expertise in the local community to extend the range of its curriculum. Here local basket weaver Kirsty Rosser helps pupil Rebecca Rodgers with her basket work.

these activities. The large age range in the school makes this separation into individuals and groups necessary much of the time, but Colin Hodgetts does not see it as a disadvantage:

> It's a different sort of teaching to the kind normally found in secondary schools where children are collected into class age groups. But there is no reason why secondary teachers shouldn't teach like primary teachers, based on project work, with each child having its own curriculum and being able to work at its own level and at its own speed. Moreover, I have the view, and by now the children seem to have accepted it, that I should not be expected to know the answers to all their questions. What I need to be able to do is to find the answers and know where they can go to find somebody who can answer their questions.

Of course, that 'somebody' can always be the child's parents, and a small but growing minority of parents in the Alternative Movement are opting for the radical course of completely deschooling their children and educating them at home. Section 36 of the 1944 Education Act says: 'It shall be the duty of the parent of every child of compulsory age to cause him to receive efficient full-time education suitable to his age, ability and aptitude, either by regular attendance at school or otherwise.' The phrase 'or otherwise' makes it clear that in the United Kingdom education is legally compulsory but schooling is not. It led to the formation, in 1978, of the group 'Education Otherwise' to act as a supporting organization for parents educating their children at home. By 1984 it had a

membership of well over 1,000 families, groups and individuals distributed widely through the United Kingdom and abroad. It has a network of more than fifty local co-ordinators spread over the country willing to give personal help to members in their area. These are backed up by people with specialized experience.

In this chapter we have looked at just two alternative schools. Many more are springing up across Britain in reaction to the deficiencies of a State education system that, after nearly forty years of development since the Second World War, is running out of ideas. Of course, not all State education is bad by definition, and there is evidence within it of regeneration and reform. Perhaps the most encouraging is the concept of the Community College, pioneered in the late 1960s by Coventry Education Committee. This is basically a comprehensive school that is deliberately run as a service for the whole community, and in this sense it embodies a holistic approach to education. Community Colleges, as well

The Rodway family educate their three children at home. Here Ruth, the older daughter learns how to spin wool provided by their own sheep.

as providing the conventional range of classes for children, open up their facilities to the whole community. Many classes are available to adults during the day, and it is not uncommon to find parents sitting alongside their children. In the evenings a whole range of further education classes are available and are often attended by the older children as well as adults. Extra facilities such as swimming pools, sports halls, squash courts, floodlit pitches, dance and movement rooms, social lounges, playgroups and crèches, are typically found in Community Colleges. Unfortunately, however, the cutbacks on education budgets within the State system since the end of the 1970s have severely limited the growth of such schools and initiatives like them.

By and large the outstanding impression given by the State education system is its uniformity. The first comprehensive school was opened by the London County Council just after the Second World War and, after prodigious effort and massive expenditure, the country is now covered with such schools. Considering that in the administration of its education Britain, by world standards, enjoys an exceptional degree of local autonomy through the local education authorities, it is extraordinary that most of these new schools should have turned out so similar, above all in their size. They are, in fact, evidence of the characteristic homogeneity and centralizing tendency of British society. It is not uncommon for between 1,500 and 2,000 children, the population of a small town, to be packed into one giant building. And this giantism has been largely decreed by the centralized Examination Boards that are the bureaucratic controllers of much that goes on in the name of education. The Alternative critique of the examination system and the education structure it inspires is that it affects children in the following harmful ways:

(a) By setting a premium on the power of merely reproducing other people's ideas and other people's methods of presentation, it diverts energy from the creative process.

(b) By rewarding evanescent — that is, quickly fading — forms of knowledge.

(c) By favouring a somewhat passive type of mind.

(d) By giving an undue advantage to those who, in answering questions on paper, can cleverly make the best use of, perhaps, slender attainments.

(e) By inducing the pupils, in their preparation for an examination, to aim rather at absorbing information imparted to them by the teacher than at forming an independent judgement upon subjects in which they receive instruction.

(f) By stimulating the competitive (and, at its worst, a mercenary) spirit in the acquisition of knowledge.

These points are not listed in the 1980s by someone allied to the Alternative Movement. They were made in 1911, by the Consultative Committee of the Board of Education on Examinations in Secondary Schools. In education, as in so much else, the Alternative Movement is merely breathing new life into old but refreshing ideas.

An academic who has made a study of alternative schools, David Reynolds, of University College, Cardiff, judged that more and more parents were opting out of the system because they saw comprehensive schools in particular as large, soulless institutions that had developed into cramming factories for examinations:

> What they are looking for in education is more emphasis on the social and emotional development of their children. Moreover, they are seeking to become more involved themselves in the education of their children. But in the State schools this tends to be discouraged because the teachers say they are the professionals and they must decide the curriculum and teaching methods. A third point is that a lot of parents regret what happens to children when they move on from primary schools to secondary schools: in the process the emphasis on creativity and group work that you get in primary schools is often lost. Many parents wish to have their children discovering things rather than being taught them; and they wish to see their children involved in groups learning to work co-operatively. But you don't tend to get these things in our large comprehensive schools.

On the positive side, however, David Reynolds told us that the attitude of the teaching establishment, and particularly the local education authorities, to the kind of alternative education experiments we have examined in this chapter is softening:

Education lecturer David Reynolds, who has made a study of alternative schools, says the Education Authorities were wary of them in the 1960s and 1970s but are now coming to realize that there are lessons they can learn from them.

> The alternative education movement really began in the late 1960s and what happened at first was that the authorities tried to discourage it — even to the extent of prosecuting some parents who attempted to educate their children themselves. They were loath, too, to grant any kind of official or efficient label to any of the alternative schools that were being set up. But as time has gone on and more and more parents — by today thousands — have opted out of the State system, education authorities have stopped worrying so much and actually in some cases asked whether there are any lessons to be learnt from the alternative schools movement.
>
> For the fact of the matter is that the State system, especially as developed in our comprehensive schools, tends to separate academic and

pastoral work. Generally there is an entirely different set of teachers — heads of year and form tutors — that deal with the pastoral, social and emotional world the children live in. But in no sense is this holistic: it's not integrating the academic and the personal aspects of child development and education.

Another aspect, of course, is that the small schools, the alternative schools, tend to benefit by their small size. So the comprehensives must learn to try and build small groups into the large units they are.

Perhaps the State schools must learn to stop viewing parents as threats. If you actually enlist the support of parents in an active way, most of all by letting them into lessons and involving them in discussions about the curriculum and so on, then the education of the children is bound to benefit, again in an holistic way.

Source Guide

In this chapter we have not attempted to survey the wide range of alternative education initiatives that can be found across Britain. Other alternative schools we might have profiled include the White Lion Free School, 57 White Lion Street, London N1 9PP, which has published *A Handbook of Alternative Education* (available from the same address); and Kirkdale School, 186 Kirkdale, London SE26. One of the founders of Kirkdale, Susie Powlesland, has published a pamphlet *No Ordinary School* and from time to time the school publishes a bulletin.

For further information on Steiner schools contact the Steiner Schools Fellowship, c/o Elmfield School, Love Lane, Stourbridge, West Midlands. If you send a stamped addressed envelope you can obtain a free booklet *What about a Steiner School?* A range of published material is available from the Rudolf Steiner Bookshop, 35 Park Road, London W1. For more information on The Small School contact The Small School, Fore Street, Hartland, Bideford, Devon.

The Community Education Development Centre at Briton Road, Coventry CV2 4LF, Tel. 0203-440814, co-ordinates information on Community Schools and publishes a monthly magazine. The Advisory Centre for Education (ACE), 18 Victoria Park Square, London E2 9PB, has promoted many conferences and publications on alternatives, generally within the State system. In 1979 the Campaign for State Supported Alternative Schools was formed and its publications are available on request from the ACE address. Every month ACE publishes a magazine *Where to find out more about Education*, available on subscription only (currently £7.50 a year).

For information on Education Otherwise contact its central address: 25 Common Lane, Hemingford Abbots, Cambridgeshire PE18 9AN.

In the field of education there is a plethora of books and pamphlets so we have not attempted to give a comprehensive reading guide here. But the following books that have impressed us should lead you in plenty of directions: *Deschooling Society* by Ivan Illich (Pelican) is a radical critique of conventional attitudes to education; *Summerhill* by A. S. Neill (Pelican) is an interesting account of a prototype alternative school; and *Teach Your Own* by John Holt (Lighthouse Books) is a comprehensive guide for anyone thinking of teaching their children at home.

HOLISTIC
HEALING

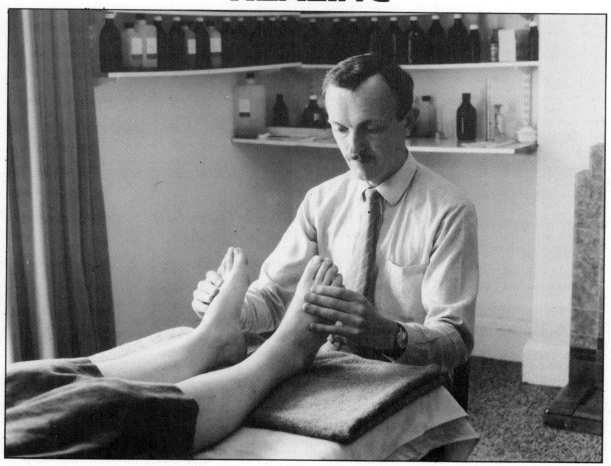

I did part of my training as an acupuncturist with a doctor in China. Sometimes when we were dining out with people he'd say to me, 'Tell them what happens in Britain if you've got a sore knee.' 'Well, the doctor treats your knee,' I'd say and everyone would fall about laughing. It was a great after-dinner joke.

Penny Brohn, co-founder of the Bristol Cancer Help Center

What Penny Brohn's Chinese colleagues found so amusing was the notion of treating a particular symptom rather than its cause. This is the fundamental difference in approach between orthodox and alternative medicine. Orthodox medicine speaks of treating and curing, whereas in alternative medicine healing is the operative word.

Alternative medicine exemplifies holism more, perhaps, than anything else we have looked at. More than energy or education, it affects us in a very personal way since we cannot divorce our health from ourselves. Holistic health is a state of balance and harmony in which every part of our being is fulfilled and in equilibrium within the whole. The emotions, intellect and spirit are involved as much as the body and must all be looked after carefully.

Healing is regarded as a process, not as an event; it involves encouraging an innate capacity for self-healing that exists within each person. The body *wants* to be well and will be if we live in tune with it.

Holism always highlights relationships, and nowhere more so than in alternative medicine. The quality of the interaction between therapist and patient is constantly stressed. We found that many alternative practitioners are interested in personal development, and that along with their treatments they will, where appropriate, give counselling to patients and encourage them to take responsibility for their own cure. This idea of self-responsibility is a striking feature of alternative medicine, and is a characteristic of the Alternative Movement as a whole. A great deal more time is allotted to consultations than in orthodox medicine. Alternative therapists feel that the very fact of having enough time to talk allows patients to unburden themselves of much of the anxiety that compounds ill health and hinders recovery.

Restoration to health is seen as a co-operative venture. Therapists give something of themselves that is as important as any actual treatment. If one wants to become a doctor the process usually starts at school, but most alternative therapists choose their profession at a more mature age and are likely to be influenced less by family tradition or the promise of status than by the fact that they want to heal people.

As well as maintaining a balance within ourselves we must live in harmony

Previous page: One of the treatments that makes use of the principles of Acupuncture is Reflexology which maintains that the energy channels Acupuncture uses link each area of the foot with an organ of the body. Reflexologist Mark Evans of the Bristol Natural Health Clinic is shown demonstrating how massaging a zone of the foot affects a different part of the body.

with other people. The interrelationships that are particularly apparent in Networking are essential to the notion of holistic health. The illness of an individual affects society, and vice versa. If we make little effort to have healthy relationships with others, then we cannot expect to be well in ourselves.

Wherever you find any kind of social initiative within the Alternative Movement you will very often discover that health is involved too. For instance, the Networking centre we visited in Bangor has a treatment room for alternative therapies. Interest in these therapies is for many people a way into deeper involvement with the alternative scene. Health food stores often provide the introduction, and the boom that they are enjoying shows the extent to which people are more conscious of how their lifestyle can affect their health. 'Natural' has become a key word in advertising campaigns, particularly where food and drink are concerned. Hence the demand for organically grown produce.

As well as living in harmony with ourselves and with other people there is a third element we need to keep in balance: our relationship with the Earth itself. The Alternative Movement has helped focus attention on the need for a clean environment and whole food. In expressing the ecological link between us and the planet some people go so far as to say that it is itself a living being, called Gaia, the ancient Greek name for the goddess of the earth. The planet is not an inert lump of material but an active entity capable of reacting when threatened. It is a form of intelligence, though not rational in our sense of the word. The

Herbal remedies are made from plants or plant extracts. Although many people take them in order to relieve symptoms, herbalism's true approach is holistic. A herbalist looks for the root cause of illness and the preparations aim to improve the standard of the patient's general health.

living being of the earth is humanity's partner in a universal scheme of evolution. Its life supports our life and its health is inseparable from ours. Gaia is characterized by an inherent unity which invites us to realize that we are made for co-operation and wholeness. We explore this concept in more detail in the final chapter. Every form of healing contributes to the evolutionary process and has positive repercussions far beyond simple physical improvements.

To many people 'healing' sounds suspiciously vague and embarrassingly personal. We have become used to the idea that one should not have to be involved in one's cure. But throughout much of the history of Western civilization, parallel to the patient's trust in doctors was a belief that medicine alone could not bring about a cure. Not only the ailing organs were involved in sickness, but a whole matrix of good and evil influences, of exterior and interior attitudes and actions. The obvious drawbacks of this belief include a tendency towards fatalism and superstition. But from the sixteenth century onwards medicine moved towards an ever more exact knowledge of the body. Objectivity became the order of the day, and the contribution of any elements that could not be scientifically measured was increasingly discounted.

One of the most influential figures in the development of medical thinking was the philosopher René Descartes. He advocated the separation of mind and body. The only irrefutable thing one can say about oneself, he held, was: 'I think, therefore I am'. Hence, logical and rational thought must be the key to all understanding. His was also the idea that the body is a machine, like a clock: 'I desire, I say, that you consider that these functions occur naturally in this machine *solely by the disposition of its organs;* not less than the movements of a clock.' The influence of the mind, therefore, was not taken into account. Descartes also held that problems were to be solved by breaking them down into their component parts, the process known as reductionism. With problems of illness, this encouraged concentration upon smaller and smaller elements — the opposite of holism.

It became increasingly easy to concentrate upon parts and 'facts' as science grew more incisive, which led to a greater understanding of disease but not of how it was affecting the patient as a whole. The attempt to find out more about this holistic picture came to seem 'unscientific'.

The Cartesian division between mind and body has been carried over into the division between those who look after the body and those who treat the mind. It is only comparatively recently that emotional factors, for instance, or stress, have been accepted as constituent parts of illness. Likewise, if disease is a natural phenomenon to be conquered, then death is the ultimate defeat. It becomes difficult to see anything positive in illness, even though it is an intimate part of the human condition. Some doctors realize that only when they have come to terms with their own mortality can they fully help their patients face up to theirs.

No one can fail to be impressed by the technical achievements of modern medicine, although there are figures to suggest that up to 25 per cent of hospital admissions are caused by medical treatment rather than by disease. Some doctors, though, feel that technology has taken over from healing. We asked Dr Glin Bennet, who was a surgeon and is now a psychiatrist, why, despite the high status of medicine, alternative therapies are expanding so fast?

> Just close to here there is an Alternative medicine clinic with 1,000 appointments a month and it is something we have got to take notice of. I think so many people are going to alternative therapists because they are dissatisified with doctors. There is something they are not getting from people like us and they are going to others. What they are getting amongst other things is attention to the whole person. You go to a doctor and he treats the part of you that is at fault. The holistic therapist takes into account the emotional and intellectual state of patients as well as their physical condition.

Often it is not the excellence of medical skill that is in question but the human factor. Faced with a tight timetable, staff feel they can only cope if they maintain a business-like attitude, but this can sometimes manifest itself to patients as a disregard for them as people. This in turn can produce a new kind of fatalism, where the patient resigns all decisions to the doctor.

Choices and Individual Needs

The Institute of Complementary Medicine (a body that co-ordinates and promotes alternative therapies) did a survey in 1983 of 500 practitioners in the five major therapies (Chiropractic, Herbalism, Acupuncture, Osteopathy and Homoeopathy) and found a 15 per cent increase in the number of treatments over the last year. These treatments take place in the consulting rooms of individual therapists, but a growing trend is for them to group together. This offers the patient a wider range of therapies under one roof. If your homoeopath thinks you could benefit from massage, say, or osteopathy, you can be referred to a colleague.

Such treatment centres have opened up all over Britain. We went to the Bristol Natural Health Clinic which has fourteen different therapies available. Apart from the main five the choice includes Massage, Alexander Technique, Aromatherapy, Yoga, Counselling and Metamorphic Technique, plus a midwife for natural childbirth advice and a dietician. Although this array is impressive there are in fact over fifty other therapies available in Britain. A number, such as Naturopathy, Hydrotherapy and Hypnotherapy, are long established in this country, whereas Gestalt, Rolfing and Radionics are relatively unfamiliar. Iridology and Kirlian Photography are examples of other alternative diagnostic techniques, and there are therapies that have been developed only recently, such as Silva Mind Control and Applied Kinesiology.

The choice can be bewildering, but all these techniques of healing are based on holistic principles and together offer a pattern of approaches from which a unique blend can be drawn to suit each individual. Holism, though it emphasizes the unity of humanity, also highlights the importance of individuals and their right to an answer that is exactly tailored to their needs. These therapies do not in themselves bring about healing but aid the self-healing capacity within each person.

The Bristol Natural Health Clinic has eighteen practitioners. Annie Du- Plessis, an acupuncturist, interviews new patients and suggests an appropriate therapy or a combination of several. Treatments last an hour. Annie might recommend that you see Mark Evans, who is a reflexologist. Reflexology is a fairly new name in Britain but is fast gaining popularity. It looks quite enjoyable. You lie down and have your feet massaged. All very soothing until . . . OW! Every organ in the body, it is said, is represented in the feet by a reflex zone. If it is painful under pressure this shows that the corresponding organ is ailing. The zones are linked to energy channels in the body and massage of the zones means you can benefit the organs, releasing tension and clearing congested energy.

Opposite: *Keith Phillips is pictured at the Bristol Natural Health Clinic, giving a patient Shiatsu treatment. Shiatsu is a Japanese therapy in which pressure is applied to acupuncture points to stimulate or regulate the body's energies. Therapists massage with their hands but also use their elbows and knees and even walk on the patient.*

Right: *cranial osteopathy is mainly a diagnostic technique. The pulse of a patient's cerebro-spinal fluid can be felt particularly clearly on the skull and pelvis. Cranial osteopaths gauge from the pulse's quality where in the body adjustments need to be made. They claim success in treating autistic children and new-born babies who have had a difficult birth.*

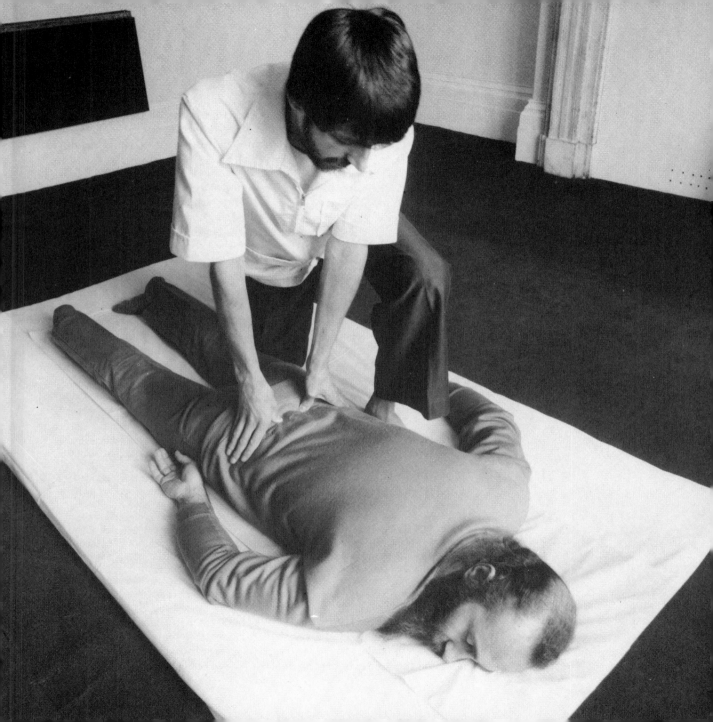

Shiatsu works on similar principles. In Japanese 'shi' means finger and 'atsu' means pressure. Pressure is applied to acupuncture points to summon energy to spots where it is needed and to disperse it from congested areas. As in acupuncture and reflexology, the area treated may be far away from the source of the complaint.

Acupuncture, Chiropractic and Homoeopathy

Acupuncture exemplifies how quickly a therapy can move from being regarded as way out to being almost run-of-the-mill. It is an ancient Chinese method of treating illness, or rather maintaining health. Natural sources of energy within the body are regulated through the insertion of very fine special needles into specific points (acupuncture points) on the body. These points are carefully selected sites that correspond to organs or body functions. This puncturing at certain points stimulates a vital or healing energy to pass along invisible channels, known as meridians, to the diseased or painful part or organ. This energy is known as 'Chi' in Chinese philosophy.

The ancient Chinese believed in the concept of whole health: a healthy mind and body for them consisted of a perfect balance of energies. The aim of traditional acupuncture is, therefore, to counter the imbalance of a sick person by treating the mind/body organism as a whole.

The Chinese concept of whole health attracted Shanee Lintott to train as an acupuncturist and she now practises in Cardiff:

> I have been interested in growth and self-development for a long time. I like the approach of traditional Chinese acupuncture, which looks at the whole person — body, mind and spirit — not just the symptoms people present, but where they're really coming from. We really try to understand the essence of that person, this human being, and we're not so much concerned with the specific distress signals that people present but what it is they're really asking for. We look at people in terms of energy imbalances where there may be blockages in energy flow. By restoring this flow, this proper balance of the whole of that system — body, mind and spirit — we restore a natural state of health. The acupuncturist is the instrument in that process. One of the most striking contrasts between this approach and conventional medicine is that we can spend time with the person. We have time to talk, to listen, to really appreciate what's going on and that is very valuable in itself.

Very often people try an alternative therapy when their doctor's resources have been exhausted. So the cases that come to a therapist are usually the chronic ones who have either heard that there is nothing more to be done or that their feeling constantly under the weather is 'psychological'. An important factor in whatever success therapists have may be that patients are often very determined to get well. After all, they have consciously chosen this treatment, are paying for it and may very well be desperate and ready to undergo discipline.

In Britain over 30,000 working days are lost each year because of back-ache, an ailment that doctors can often do little to help. Fortunately, both Osteopathy and Chiropractic are becoming increasingly 'respectable' in the eyes of the medical profession. In the Institute of Complementary Medicine's survey, Chiropractic showed the biggest increase in numbers of patients. Practitioner Simon Leyson explained:

> Chiropractic is an independent branch of medicine dealing particularly with mechanical disorders of the spine and pelvis. We help lumbago, sciatica, neck pain and the like. We differ from osteopathy in technique to a small

Acupuncturist Shanee Lintott, pictured here, was attracted by the therapy's holistic approach. Acupuncture needles like the one shown are inserted at spots known as 'acupuncture points' along invisible energy channels in the body to balance its vital forces.

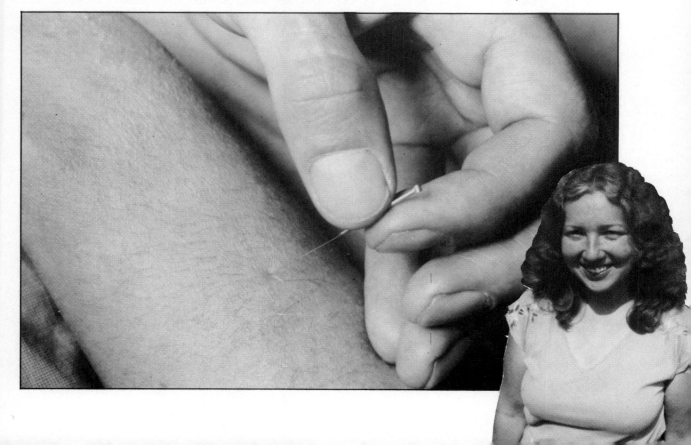

extent, and we use more X-rays and radiological investigation. . . When you are manipulating the spine you have to have a good idea of what is present. That's why we have a system of examination which tests out those structures in the back and neck and also finds out whether there is any other disease present which we cannot treat. For instance, an X-ray may show that one of the vertebrae has been partly destroyed. Now, if you manipulated that, it would be very, very serious for the patient, so we refer this patient to a medical specialist to deal with this type of problem.

Osteopathy and Chiropractic are forms of treatment based on manipulation, which aims at removing structual stresses and improving body functions. Both types of practitioners deal mostly with back problems, including slipped discs, arm and shoulder pain, headaches and other musculo-skeletal pains. Because of the nerve connections from the spine, Osteopaths and

More working days are lost in Britain each year because of back ache than through any other single ailment. An osteopath corrects structural disorders of the muscles and joints by manipulation.

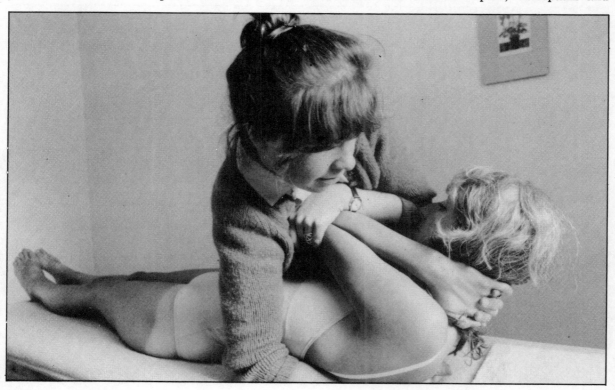

Chiropractors are also able to help with some kinds of migraine, asthma, digestive and menstrual problems, arthritis, and emotional and stressful conditions. They will often also advise on diet, exercise and rest.

Osteopathy is better known and more readily available in this country, but throughout the world chiropractic is more widely practised. Non-medical Osteopaths sometimes use naturopathic or Homoeopathic remedies to supplement manipulation.

Chiropractors and Osteopaths worry about the damage caused by 'cowboys'. Under British law there is nothing to stop anyone setting up as any kind of therapist, so the public should *always* check on the practitioner's training before proceeding for treatment. There is no need to fear that one is being rude. Any practitioner worth his or her salt will welcome evidence that the public is aware of the necessity to check on standards. At the end of this chapter we provide addresses of the main representative bodies of the various therapies. They expect their members to follow professional guidelines. These include a rule of no advertising beyond an announcement that a practice is opening and an entry in the Yellow Pages of the telephone directory, which by itself is no guarantee of anything concerning standards or ability. A rule of thumb is: if there is any brash advertising, be suspicious. We came across an acupuncturist with an impressive series of letters after his name indicating he was a graduate of a college of acupuncture. After a little investigation we found that *he* was the college. So there's no harm in asking to see a training prospectus if you're uneasy.

Homoeopathy is one of alternative medicine's most intriguing therapies. The name comes from two Greek words: *homoios,* meaning 'similar', and *pathos,* meaning 'suffering'. Homoeopathy was founded by Dr Samuel Hahnemann, who was born in Meissen in Saxony in 1755. He felt that the crude medical practices of his day often did more harm than good, so he looked for a method of treatment that would be both effective and safe. He had a genius for methodical observation. He saw that when healthy people took belladonna, the deadly nightshade plant, for example, they showed all the symptoms of scarlet fever. Yet a dose of the same plant given to someone really suffering from this disease produced a cure.

Experiments convinced Hahnemann that whatever in large doses produces the symptoms of a disease will, in small doses, cure that disease. This is the basic principle of Homoeopathy, that 'Like cures like'. To orthodox medicine symptoms are the unpleasant results of disease, but to Homoeopathy symptoms are signs that a natural healing force in the body is working against disease; thus Homoeopathic medicine does not repress symptoms — it encourages them.

Hahnemann noted that since no two people react to a disease in the same

Paediatrician Dr David Lewis is the only consultant in a National Health Service hospital who uses homoeopathy in his work. He is shown here examining Marisa Stephens who, until she received homoeopathic treatment, suffered from chronic hay-fever.

way, treatment should be tailored to the individual, seeing them holistically and taking into account many features, including temperament and tastes. Even one's complexion, fair or dark, is an indication as to which remedy is appropriate. He sought to establish the smallest effective dose in order to avoid side affects. He found that the more the remedy was *diluted* the more effective it became.

Dr David Lewis works in Bronglais Hospital in Aberystwyth. We asked him how unusual it is to find a consultant paediatrician like him practising Homoeopathy in an NHS hospital:

> I am told by the Homoeopathic faculty that I am unique but I am not sure whether I'm proud of that or not. I think it is very sad because I have found Homoeopathy increasingly useful, not only in the range of conditions I treat but also in giving insight into the enormous variety of child types and personalities that I'm now much more aware of.

Because of the mysterious paradox of Homoeopathic medicines — notably their aim to cure despite containing no chemically detectable trace of the active element — they are often accused of being effective only as placebos, that is, people get better because they believe they are getting better.

All the alternative therapies maintain that they work in conjunction with a natural healing force present in the patient. They see themselves as helping this force reassert itself — a process of healing, therefore, coming as much as possible from inside outwards. The concept of healing figures much more prominently in alternative medicine than in orthodox. This is in line with the holistic impulse that is active throughout the Alternative Movement. The aim of these therapies is not to restore the status quo that existed before illness but to restore the person to wholeness — a much more comprehensive and long-term goal.

The Cancer Help Centre

The Cancer Help Centre in Bristol is a good example of the holistic approach to disease. It was set up because of firmly-held beliefs that there were ways of treating cancer that were not being exploited by orthodox medicine; in particular, that the emotional, environmental and stress factors were not being fully taken into account. Dr Alec Forbes was formerly a consultant physician but became dissatisfied with the NHS and left to help set up the Centre in 1980. He and his staff maintain that wholeness can be achieved even by people with a terminal illness. The fact that no cure as yet exists for their disease is an element that they try to bring into balance with every other part of their lives. They manage to live in equilibrium with the disease. They become, in Dr Forbes's words, 'well cancer patients'.

The type of treatment offered in the Centre differs markedly from that found is most hospitals. Nevertheless, Dr Forbes emphasized that the Centre's holistic approach need not conflict with orthodox treatment:

> The main thing is for patients to realize that they are responsible for themselves, and they should start to mobilise their inner resources and self-healing. Of course we employ therapists as well. Really, one is bringing a lot of different forces to bear upon a particular situation from many different angles and that is what holism is.

To help mobilize patients' inner healing force the Centre offers relaxation and breathing classes as well as psychotherapy and counselling. Biofeedback (where a meter connected to the patient shows the rise and fall of heart rate corresponding to tension or calmness) helps to train people to achieve a meditative state in which they can imagine themselves getting well again. Such visualization, as it is called, is intended to help the mind influence the body. Patients are also encouraged to give full rein to their creativity because foiling it suppresses their vital energies. According to Dr Forbes, most of us consume up to three pounds of chemicals a year; so a raw vegetable diet is a major factor in treatment to eliminate poisons and increase physical efficiency.

Healing in a variety of forms is available, such as spiritual, faith and magnetic healing; these, as Dr Forbes put it, 'refresh the parts other therapies do not reach!' He explained:

> It's very difficult to give a simple answer as to what healing is, because if you talk to healers you find that each one of them thinks they do it in a somewhat different way according to their experience, belief, capacities, understanding and the patient's needs. One of the common things is that you have to have a sort of union with the person you wish to heal. It's very like the fact that when you stand close to somebody you love, and you and your vibes unite, you get a good feeling. Healers have to be quite good at joining with people in this way. When they are in this state they can often feel what the other person is feeling, because they are so close to them that there is a sort of union between the two. That takes place first. And then the patient must *want* to get well; they don't have to believe that the healer will do them any good, they may be quite sceptical, but they have got to truly want to get better, because that desire to change and get well sucks the energy into them.
>
> The next move is for the healer to get into a sort of centred state and make a request — you could call it prayer, but in any case an effort of will that energy should come into this person you are trying to heal according to their needs; not according to what they want to be done or you think ought to be done but what the person needs. So it's best to be absolutely non-specific. Then you can be aware that there is a sort of flow of energy taking place through you to the other person. Sometimes you aren't aware of anything; sometimes both are aware of a certain state of peace — sometimes of warmth, sometimes of cool — it varies with the conditions and requirements of the people involved. After a while you feel that that's gone on long enough and so you stop the process. There are many variations on how you can do this, according to techniques and different teachings, but that is the general principle of it.

Penny Brohn, who helped start the Centre, is convinced of the intimate link between mind and body. She suffered from breast cancer but recovered:

> It's quite amazing how for six months I sort of lived in terror. I used to come home and suddenly a great fear would come over me — I'm dying! It was tragic. Before the doctor told me I had cancer I was fine. The moment he told me I had cancer I decided that I had got to die — to conform, you know. I

used to go home and go running into the bedroom and sit between the wardrobe and the wall and scream with fear. But I learnt that *I* had to do something and it wasn't so much my diet — that was nothing to me — but I had to overcome something and I know it was a word. Once I came to terms with the word 'cancer' my cancer was cured.

Alternative Medicine and Orthodoxy

Medicine is an area where the Alternative Movement has clashed particularly stridently with conventional interests. There is a lot of money involved in medicine, in general practice as well as pharmaceutical companies. Alternative medicine is queering the traditional pitch. It has spawned industries of its own and drawn money away from conventional drugs. Most of all it has encouraged

Left: *Diet is an essential feature of treatment at the Bristol Cancer Help Centre. Only vegetarian food is served. This helps rid patients' systems of toxins and increases their vitality.*
Below: *Dr Alex Forbes and Penny Brohn are two of the co-founders of the Centre. Dr Forbes is the Centre's medical director.*

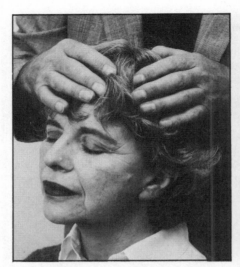 

The Bristol Cancer Help
Centre regards stress as
a major cause of cancer.
Several techniques are
used to help patients cope
with stress. A patient is
shown here using a Bio-
feedback machine which
graphically demonstrates
the effect the mind has
on the body and so helps
patients learn how to
relax. They also attend
relaxation classes like the
one shown below. Several
forms of healing, such as
the faith healing pictured
here, are available.

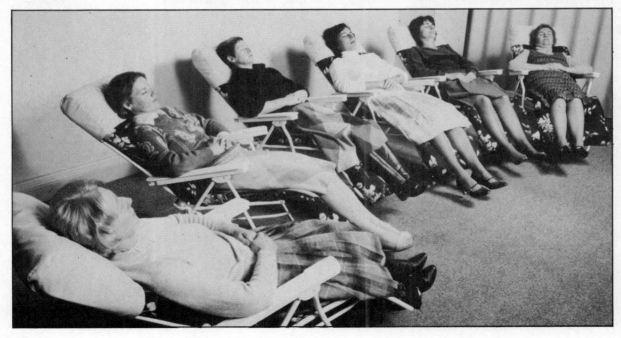

doubt in their efficacy. This growth brings dangers of its own. Self-dosing with an improperly identified product from a health store could be worse than conventional drug treatment.

Orthodox practitioners worry about the lack of scientific proof concerning alternative medicine. In 1983 the British Medical Association set up an inquiry into its value. It invited doctors and lay therapists to submit information on the therapies themselves, on whether they are used alone or in association with conventional treatments, and on how they are believed to work. The aim was to assess the value of the therapies in helping patients. Three hundred people responded and it stimulated a lot of discussion among alternative practitioners, who in general reacted with a mixture of approval of the initiative and distrust of the motives and of the assessment methods. There was doubt in particular as to whether anyone in the BMA Working Party was sufficiently experienced in alternative medicine.

The BMA revealed that pressure from its president, the Prince of Wales, had been a significant factor in the setting up of the inquiry. An editorial in *The Lancet* of October 1983 responded to this:

> Particularly significant perhaps was a comment by Prince Charles that 'what is taken for today's unorthodoxy is probably going to be tomorrow's convention'. Alternatively, perhaps, yesterday's plausible explanation may only survive as today's straw to be clutched by the distressed and the desperate... If the major task of the new committee is to review hard scientific evidence on the benefits of alternative medicine its deliberations will be brief indeed.

The editorial warned of the dangers of evidence for efficacy that was based on anecdote, on improvement in cases where the illness was known to have a fluctuating course, or where psychosomatic causes had not been sufficiently taken into account. It recognised the challenge that is being presented to the medical profession:

> How often do orthodox medical practitioners offer care that likewise lacks scientific proof? . . . If concern for the individual, sympathetic understanding and reassurance are too poorly developed (within orthodox medicine) to offer an alternative to phony pseudoscientific constructions, this requires urgent attention in its own right. Such an outlook does not need to be graced with the term 'holistic medicine': it is simply the practice of treating patients as they should be treated by an adequately trained physician. If patients are resorting in increasing numbers to practices based upon the obsolescent relics of the prehistory of modern medicine this requires urgent attention. In

that case, the subject of the next BMA investigating committee should be contemporary orthodox medical practice.

Part of the problem in the relationship between the two approaches to medicine is that doctors are not well informed about alternatives. A survey was carried out in 1983 among a hundred general practitioner trainees; it was entitled 'Young Doctors' Views on Alternative Medicine'. There was a high degree of open-mindedness to the therapies, with 80 per cent wishing to train in at least one method and about 21 per cent already using one. Hypnosis was the most popular and it happens to be the one that is most established within orthodox medicine. It was also the one to which the greatest number of doctors made referrals.

The report commented that all this contrasted with 'the picture frequently painted by the media of narrow-minded, drug-oriented doctors driving the public to alternative practitioners'. It warned alternative therapists not to fall into the very trap for which they criticize the orthodox: over-specialization; that is, going to a hypnotherapist for one thing and a herbalist for another, and so on. It concluded:

> The whole person needs a whole doctor who can assess his whole problem and who can refer him to a specialist, if required. Based on the data gathered here, it is clear that young doctors view these methods not as alternative approaches but as complementary to more orthodox approaches.

The confrontation between orthodox and alternative medicine has produced some curious reactions. On the one hand the alternative therapies want to maintain their independence; on the other they would like to achieve recognition as 'professions supplementary to medicine'. Thus the British Chiropractic Association applied for recognition in 1976 which would have enabled them to work within the NHS and to receive training grants. It would also have made it more difficult for improperly qualified people to practise.

The alternative therapists are just as concerned to bar from practice those whom they consider unqualified as the orthodox. They fear that the medical profession, since it cannot stop their growth, is trying to control them through annexation. There has been mixed reaction to the formation in 1983 of the British Holistic Medical Association, which took as its motto 'Physician Heal Thyself'. This reads like an invitation to doctors to put their own house in order.

The fact that such an association has been formed by eminent doctors shows the extent to which the concept of holism has made inroads in the profession. The Association's aims are to educate, inform and research on holistic medicine and to encourage co-operation. Initially membership was restricted only to medically-trained personnel, but in the autumn of 1983 associate membership was offered to lay therapists. Their response was mixed. Some welcomed the chance of greater co-operation with doctors who are thinking along the same lines, but there is also a fear that it is a move to exploit their expertise and eventually absorb them — the fear being that if doctors become masters of these therapies they will try to establish a monopoly over them. Only time will reveal whether or not there is any substance to these suspicions.

Of the 28,800 general practitioners (1982 figure) in Britain, so far only 350 have chosen to join the new Holistic Medical Association. So there is a long way to go before the profession could be said to be changing as a whole. However, the results of an inquiry organized by the British Postgraduate Medical Foundation in 1983/84 into holistic medicine show that it is possible to put holistic principles into operation in general practice. It looked at how doctors treat their patients, and the contribution that their own health and personal development make to these relationships. The survey found that the more a doctor adopted a holistic approach the better the results.

Holistic healing must be one of the most attractive features of the Alternative Movement, though it existed long before anyone began to formulate alternative approaches. It demonstrates the person-centred approach of holism particularly clearly, since it highlights the therapeutic potential of person-to-person contact. Holistic healing stresses the harmony that ought to exist within us, in our relations with other people and with the whole of creation. It is eminently practical and yet open to spiritual influences in its insistence on an inner principle of growth and healing. Through its compassionate attention to the cause rather than to the symptoms of disease it avoids the trap into which conventional medicine so often falls: putting the technology of treatment between the patient and true healing.

As it constantly challenges us to assume responsibility for our own health, so alternative medicine inevitably pushes us to choose the kind of life we want. The realization that we can choose to change is a fundamental thrust of the Alternative Movement. It is especially obvious in the area of healing. Just as we can choose to be well instead of ill, so we can choose to co-operate rather than to compete, to live in harmony with the environment instead of dominating and eventually destroying it.

Holistic healing demands a revolution in our attitudes to illness. Far from regarding illness as a negative experience, alternative medicine sees each sickness as an opportunity for taking stock and discovering new creative energies that had previously been untapped.

Source Guide

The following list gives the main contacts for the major complementary therapies. All these bodies will supply details of training and a register of practitioners on request. Enclose an S.A.E.

ACUPUNCTURE:

British Acupuncture Association
34, Alderney St
LONDON SW1V 4EU
Membership restricted to those with medical training, including veterinary medicine, Osteopathy and naturopathy.

Traditional Acupuncture Society
Tao House
Queensway
ROYAL LEAMINGTON SPA
Warwickshire CB32 5EZ

British Academy of Western
Acupuncture
12 Rodney St
LIVERPOOL L1 2TE
Membership restricted to doctors, dentists and nurses.

International College of Oriental
Medicine
Green Hedges House
Green Hedges Avenue
EAST GRINSTEAD
Sussex RH10 1DZ

HOMOEOPATHY:

The Homoeopathic Development
Foundation
19A Cavendish Square
LONDON W1M 9AD

British Homoeopathic Association
27A Devonshire Street
LONDON W1N 1RJ
Can provide names and addresses of general practitioners who provide Homoeopathic treatment privately and of NHS pharmacies providing Homoeopathic remedies.

The Hahnemann Society
217 Coldharbour Lane
LONDON SW9 8RU
Publishes a magazine, Homoeopathy Today, *and has lists of stockists.*

The Society of Homoeopaths
101 Sebastian Avenue
Shenfield
BRENTWOOD
Essex CM15 8PP
A society of professional Homoeopaths who are not medical practitioners. Has a register of members.

OSTEOPATHY:

General Council and Register of
Osteopaths
1-4 Suffolk Street
LONDON SW1Y 4HG

British and European Osteopathic
Association
Orient House
42–45 New Broad Street
LONDON EC2M 1QY
Has a register of qualified practitioners from several schools of Osteopathy in Britain and Europe.

British Osteopathic Association
8-10 Boston Place
LONDON NW1 6QH
An association for doctors

Society of Osteopaths
12 College Road
EASTBOURNE
East Sussex
BN21 4HZ
Has a register of qualified practitioners.

British Naturopathic and
Osteopathic Association
Frazer House
6 Netherall Gardens
LONDON NW3
A college and clinic. Has a register of qualified naturopaths and Osteopaths.

CHIROPRACTIC:

British Chiropractic Association
5 First Avenue
CHELMSFORD
Essex CM1 1RX

HERBALISM:

National Institute of Medical
Herbalists
The Registrar
148 Forest Road
TUNBRIDGE WELLS
Kent
For details of training and prospectus enclose £1 and a large SAE

The Herb Society
34 Boscobel Place
LONDON SW1
General information on herbs.

The Dr Edward Bach Centre
Mount Vernon
SOTWELL
Wallingford
Oxon OX10 0PX

Has a register of practitioners and will also send remedies, books and advice on The Bach treatment, which uses a range of 38 remedies derived from plants.

The Institute for Complementary Medicine
21 Portland Place
LONDON W1N 3AF
An information service for enquiries on various forms of complementary medicine. Send SAE for a list of practitioners in your area and remember to state the kind of therapy you wish to investigate.

NATUROPATHY:

Naturopathy is concerned with finding and removing the cause of disease whether it be:

1. *Chemical*
from faulty eating, drinking, breathing or elimination
2. *Mechanical*
spinal malalignments, muscular tension, sprained ligaments and stiff joints or bad posture.
3. *Psychological*
anxieties, frustrations, fears, etc.

Treatment will almost invariably include advice on diet but may also include a prescription for herbal or homoeopathic medicines and vitamin supplements. If necessary spinal manipulations will be carried out.

British Naturopathic and Osteopathic Association
6 Netherall Gardens
LONDON NW3 5RR

HYPNOSIS AND PSYCHOTHERAPY:

People can be referred to psychotherapists in the NHS by their GPs or can refer themselves (though they will be asked to allow their GP to give them a medical check).

It should be noted that it is legal to practise hypnosis and psychotherapy without any form of training. There are, however, lay practitioners who have been properly trained:

British Society of Experimental and Clinical Hypnosis
c/o Dr Michael Heap
Psychology Service
St Augustine's Hospital
CHARTHAM
Nr Canterbury
Kent
An association of qualified practitioners of hypnosis. Its membership consists of psychologists, physicians and dentists. Will give names of practitioners in your area.

British Society of Dental and Medical Hypnosis
42 Linke Road
ASHTEAD
Surrey KT21 2HY
The Society keeps a list of members in various parts of the country who are willing to accept patients for treatment with hypnosis. Patients must be referred through their own doctors. Send SAE bearing your GP's name and address (not yours) and the society will let your GP have the names of any practitioners in your area.

The British Association of Psychotherapists
121 Hendon Lane
LONDON N3 3 PR
This association provides training in psychotherapy and has a register of trained and approved therapists.

Association of Hypnotists and Psychotherapists
Blythe Tutorial College
25 Market Square
NELSON
Lancs
The college offers training for both the medically qualified and the lay person. The Association keeps a register of practitioners.

Association of Child Psychotherapists
Burgh House
New End Square
LONDON NW3
This is the only organization for child psychotherapists.

REFLEXOLOGY:

International Institute of Reflexology
P.O. Box 34
HARLOW
Essex CM17 0LT

British School of Reflex Zone Therapy of the Feet
25 Brooks Mews
LONDON W1Y 1LF

Miscellaneous:

Touch for Health Foundation
39 Browns Road
SURBITON
Surrey

Shiatsu Society
3 Elia Street
LONDON N2

British Wheel of Yoga
80 Lechampton Road
CHELTENHAM
Gloucester

The Bristol Cancer Help Centre
Grove House
Cornwallis Grove
Clifton
BRISTOL BS8 4PG

The Natural Health Network
Chardstock House
CHARD
Somerset
TA20 2TL
Can provide information on Natural Health Centres around the country, though not every N.H.C. is registered with them.

British Holistic Medical
Association
179 Gloucester Place
LONDON NW1 6DX
Membership is open only to doctors but associate membership is available to lay people. Plans are under consideration for the formation of a British Association for Holistic Health which would be open to other practitioners. A decision may be reached by the end of 1984. The Association has a list of doctors and publishes the British Journal of Holistic Medicine. It also organizes conferences, workshops and lectures.

The Institute for Complementary
Medicine
21 Portland Place
LONDON W1N 3AF
Publicizes natural therapies, encourages co-operation and research. It has an information library and publishes newsletters. It runs Provincial Information Points manned by volunteers who have lists of local alternative practitioners.

The following books are helpful:

A Gentle Way with Cancer by Brenda Kidman (Century, 1983).
On the work of the Bristol Cancer Help Centre.

The Alternative Health Guide by Brian Inglis and Ruth West (Michael Joseph, 1983).
Outlines 70 therapies and has a very useful bibliography.

The Turning Point by Fritjof Capra (Fontana Paperbacks, 1983).
On the cultural shift that is affecting Western society including medicine.

The Holistic Herbal by David Hoffmann (Findhorn Press, 1983).
A very comprehensive guide to herbalism with an excellent opening chapter on the holistic approach to life in general.

Alternative Medicine by Andrew Stanway (Macdonald and Janes, 1979).
A survey of a range of therapies.

Holistic Health: How to Understand and Use the Revolution in Medicine by Lawrence LeShan (Turnstone Press, 1984).
Written in America but very relevant for Britain.

The Homoeopathic Handbook (Wigmore Publications, 1984).
Available from The Homoeopathic Development Foundation. Contains details of the use of homoeopathic medicines, lists of stockists and practitioners and comprehensive information on the whole area.

CO-OPERATIVE LIVING

Human nature is incredibly weak and people living in communities have just as many faults as people in ordinary society. To have lifted ourselves out of a pretty destructive capitalist society and to have survived for five to ten years (or more) in close co-operative living and working conditions, in spite of our personal weakness, is in itself a significant achievement.

Pete West, Glaneirw House Community, 1984.

Co-operation is a key word of the Alternative Movement. Though it implies a criticism of the competitive nature of conventional society, the idea is generally seen in more practical terms of devising new ways of working and living. Workers' co-operatives in which each person involved receives equal shares of the work, worry and profit are one expression. But more fundamental are the various forms of communal living that have been evolving as an integral part of the Alternative Movement since the 1960s.

Communal living is at once the most difficult, challenging, controversial, and idealistic component of the Movement's prescription for an alternative society. At one level it is a reaction against the tendency of Western industrial societies to separate people from each other. The extended family is dying, and single parent families are booming. The nuclear family, defined as a married couple and perhaps some children, is the norm. Yet its stability is being threatened, with divorce climbing beyond a rate of one marriage in every three.

The communal living experiments that were precipitated by the experience of the 1960s and which have now evolved into the 1980s are about much more than questioning the value and stability of one-to-one marital ties. Rather, the most urgent matter they are addressing is how to find ways of harmoniously resolving the conflicts that arise within groups. On a global scale conflict resolution is the human family's most pressing need. The Alternative Movement of the 1960s was born in the shadow of the nuclear threat, and this remains central to its motivation. Therein lies the most essential role of the communal groups and housing co-operatives we shall be considering in this chapter; for if ways cannot be found of diverting conflict into constructive channels among small groups such as these, what hope is there for containing and controlling conflict in the wider political sphere? In one perspective the whole of the Alternative Movement is designed to help create the conditions for successful conflict resolution.

One of the communities we visited is based at The Centre for Alternative Technology at Machynlleth in mid-Wales. As discussed in Chapter 1, this is one of the major points of contact between the Alternative Movement and the public, and is most usually associated with demonstrating renewable energy sources. What is less commonly appreciated is that the heart of the Alternative

Previous page: *A break for tea at the Centre for Alternative Technology, Machynlleth. It is little realized that as well as acting as an exhibition centre for alternative energy and organic gardening, the Centre's thirty personnel live communally in a further effort to practise the alternative lifestyle they are prescribing for society. Everyone at the Centre earns the same wage, with different levels for single people and married couples with children. So the community effectively income-shares as well.*

Technology Centre is a community of people experimenting with a communal lifestyle. The opening paragraph of the Centre's founding statement makes the point:

> The belief behind alternative technology is that the earth belongs equally to everything now living and yet unborn. Alternative technology provides the tools for *communal self-sufficiency,* without sacrificing comfort, without waste, without depleting non-renewable resources and without harming the environment. It is the means of saving the earth from ecological catastrophe.

Conflict resolution, as practised by a range of alternative communities, has developed a common set of pre-conditions: decision-making through consensus and an absence of continued leadership by one individual; equality of status as opposed to hierarchy, generally related to income-sharing on the basis of need rather than rewards scaled to position; an emphasis on the role of women in parallel with men.

All this is not mere ideology. It is important to recognize that this theoretical identity has grown very much out of practical experience. The point can be made by quoting how some of the communes operating in Britain today describe themselves when seeking new members. Thus a small commune in Burnley, Lancashire, 'People in Common', writing in the *Communes Network* magazine in 1984:

> At present we are six adults and four children living in six terraced houses and have room for three more people. We try to be non-sexist, anarchistic, co-operative, humorous and non-violent. Mostly (sometimes, say pessimists) we succeed. We all help to run a crèche during work hours, for our children, to enable both men and women to care for children and to earn money to pay their way within the group. We also take turns to cook and clean in the main house/office, which is two terraced houses next to each other. We usually do money-earning three days a week. We pool all our income. Some of us are interested in home education in the future and belong to Education Otherwise. We help to run a local food co-op which is based on one of our houses.
>
> We have an old corn mill seven miles away outside the town, which we intend to convert into a variety of living and working spaces, some communal, some personal. This will give some of us an opportunity to live a more rural and communal life, though some of us may stay here and form the nucleus of a continuing town-based group.

Another group, 'Some People in Leicester Community', writing in the same issue of the magazine, declared that it too was seeking new members, people willing to join its committed core group:

> Membership of the core group involves committment to full collectivity which embraces such principles as: co-operation, stewardship, mutual accountability, matching power to responsibility, rejection of the nuclear family and exclusive emotional couples, active alternative culture building. We are committed to establishing a second (rural) base in Eire, and ask that people who join us share that vision.

The motivation for the community wishing to expand into a base in Eire provides a revealing glimpse into the thinking of the Alternative Movement. Writing in a previous issue of the magazine one of the Leicester community explained:

> For me there are a number of reasons why it is a far more conducive country than Britain in which to follow an alternative lifestyle. The actual size of the country is very small, so people and places are easily accessible. The relatively low population (three-and-a-half million with one-and-a-quarter million in Dublin) means there is more chance of your voice being heard — particularly a collective voice — on political issues, and your actions being effective.
>
> Widespread Catholicism means that people tend towards conservatism in moral issues — marriage, the family, the role of women — but many, especially younger, people now question these beliefs. For example, the Amendment referendum took place during our recent visit, and the debate between anti- and pro-abortionists had raised the consciousness of many people (it was a rare treat to hear ageing Irish men vehemently discussing the subject of women's wombs over pints of Guinness in the bars!).
>
> Western civilization's obsession with consumerism has yet to take over people's lives and minds — except perhaps in Dublin — so they seemed far more open to ideas about collectivity and caring communities; the word 'community' still has real meaning for them.

Peter Raine, Director of the Centre for Alternative Technology, believes that the commune movement has changed radically since the 1960s: 'Lots of people got into it thinking it was the answer to everything and weren't prepared for all the problems. Today I think there's a second wind. Many of us in the commune movement are the same people as in the 1960s but we're older and wiser.'

Interest in communal living burgeoned in the wake of the 1960s protest movements, particularly against American involvement in Vietnam, that developed into a general critique of capitalist consumerist society. Many young people, often students, enthusiastically embraced communal living as a way of 'dropping out' from conventional society. It was a time of great interest but little action, of the creation but rapid withering of many initiatives. Within a few years, towards the end of the 1970s, the movement was hit by the recession and a new mood of austerity inimical to radical change. The commune movement seemed to have run out of steam. But by the mid-1980s the movement appears to have gained fresh impetus. Tempered by hard experience it is exploring less ambitious but more practical and stable forms of co-operative living than those that typified the late 1960s and early 1970s. And though there are fewer people engaged in the enterprise, more of them are actually active in direct, meaningful ways. In the early 1970s the magazine about communal living of that period had a circulation of around 3,500 copies, yet there were perhaps half a dozen genuine communes in existence in Britain. By the mid-1980s the equivalent magazine, *Communes Network,* had a circulation of less than 300, but some 40 communes were in being and about 300 housing co-operatives.

The 1980s movement is tougher, more disciplined, structured and organized, and more survivalist than its counterpart of the early 1970s. Typically, it is peopled by middle-class people who have felt the pressures of the recession — ex-social workers, teachers, nurses, architects — who have lost job motivation and are seeking a more meaningful personal lifestyle. Typically, too, they will have lived in urban centres, probably in the south-east of England, and are seeking a more rural environment, often in the west. At the same time they tend to be in their thirties, the age-group that was formed by the 1960s. Often they may have lived through the experience of the commune movement of that era and grown as a result. The connections have not all been lost, nor the idealism. Looking back, the atmosphere of the commune movement of the early 1970s was well caught by Gerard Morgan-Grenville, one of the founders of the Centre for Alternative Technology. In 1973 he visited the United States, 'because most of the "alternative" literature was emanating from there', and was struck by the extent to which the hippies of that period had succeeded in escaping from the System:

> The hippie-communes that I visited in California were, in varying degrees, unsuccessful. An anarchic commune, consisting principally of unskilled couples, mostly in their twenties, often of transient loyalties to each other and the commune, apathetic about hard work, serves as an education as to how Mankind could slip quietly back to the Stone Age. But for all the hopelessness and helplessness that characterized so many dropped-out individuals or groups, there were other ingredients which compensated for their obvious failings. Often a transparent, almost infectious honesty showed in the way they thought and lived. They recognized the State's army of bureaucrats as being social parasites and if the dole was accepted, it was because they were antagonistic to the uses to which public funds were put. They lived close to the earth, exploiting no-one, and they found satisfaction that their simplicity of living caused no strain on the environment. They refused to take work which resulted in the manufacture of products that they felt were socially or environ-mentally bad. In many ways the good in these people shone forth but their way of living was extremely fragile and there was a tendency for groups to disintegrate rapidly.

Felicity Shooter, another member of the Centre's Community, known as the Tea Chest, says that relationships between the sexes in communes tend to become like that of brothers and sisters: 'When you work and live together you get very close, sharing problems and feelings. It makes working together a lot easier because you understand what's going on in their home life.'

The communities highlighted in this chapter — the Glaneirw House Community, a commune with eight adults and three children in west Wales, and the Rainbow Housing Co-operative of 33 adults and a dozen children in Milton Keynes — in their different ways illustrate how far co-operative living has progressed since the 1960s. Although both evolved out of the impetus and idealism of the 1960s, both reflect the harder, more realistic atmosphere of the 1980s.

The Glaneirw House Community

The Glaneirw House Community began in 1975 with eight people who wanted to establish a largely self-sufficient community in which members lived and

Glaneirw House was built as a mansion, became a hotel and was empty for three years before it became the home of a commune in 1975. In the foreground are Jeannie Averill and Pete West with their daughter Ceri.

worked collectively. They pooled their financial resources and, with the help of a £5,000 bank loan, bought a seventeen-bedroom mansion and surrounding 44 acres for £36,000 at an auction in Cardigan. Situated at Blaenporth, two miles from the coast, it was formerly a hotel but had been empty for three years. Several of the founder members had begun the move from their former lifestyle by working on farms as WWOOFers (people who spend Working Weekends on Organic Farms: see Chapter One). One, who had also been in the Merchant Navy, had worked more extensively on farms, particularly in Devon. Another had owned a farm in Wales. The rest came from occupations that had little connection with the land: the law, nursing, computer programming, academic research. Several had dropped out of university and a few had travelled widely in India and Africa. All, in their different ways, were searching for an alternative to the conventional plan which seemed marked out for them.

The first two years or so were a struggle, purely for survival. There was no money income and initially no crops were growing. A shop was established on the premises to sell vegetables and other produce to visitors. A pottery was set up and this extended the range of goods for sale. But the lack of a dependable source of cash income proved a continuing headache. The community had been set up as a trust with four trustees who were founder members. Within the first two years four of the founder members left and, under the trust, were paid the amount they had invested in three equal instalments over three years, starting with an initial £500 on their departure. The property was valued annually and the equity shared. All this placed an additional strain on the remaining members. It soon became clear that, with the sharp increases in property values, repayments on the equity would become prohibitive. For this reason, and with the political aim of avoiding individual profit, it was agreed to make the trust non-equity sharing: on leaving members agreed to withdraw only the capital they had put in.

These financial pressures were the root of many of the personality clashes that afflicted the community during this period. None of the founder members had had any extended experience of living communally, and their difficulties were accentuated by the large number of short-stay visitors who came to the community. One member who joined during this period and is still a member of the community commented: 'You would sit down at meal times and most probably not know the name or background of the person sitting next to you.' Decision-making was originally by consensus, but eventually it was agreed on a three-quarter majority vote when consensus failed. Gradually even this became difficult as internal divisions in the group deepened. One fundamental source of conflict was over vegetarianism. Most sympathized with this approach to eating,

Top left: The Community's first task is to maintain its 44-acre organic farm, which is run under the direction of one of the longest-serving members, Doug Bransden.

Bottom left: The Community's main source of income is from a plumbing service it offers centred round the adaptation of solid fuel heaters for central heating. Annemieke Snidjers prefers this work to any other, though everybody mixes in with the domestic chores.

Top right: Pottery is another source of income, mainly in the summer from passing tourist trade. Leslie Kahn, seen here, is in charge.

Bottom right: The Community is largely self-sufficient in food with a mainly vegetarian diet. Cheese-making is a daily routine task, shared in rotation — here under the guiding hand of Helen Steele, a former teacher from London.

but carried to extremes it undermined farm production which, because it relied heavily on milk production, necessarily entailed the slaughtering of bull calves.

Internal conflicts brought Glaneirw to a standstill in October 1980. It was agreed that five members should leave for three months, leaving a neutral member, a trustee and a long-term visitor to look after the community and allow re-assessment of the future. But when the five members returned, conflicts flared again and in September 1981, with large outstanding debts and insoluble problems, the trustees, with the consent of all the members, decided to sell the property.

By this time a group of seven long-term visitors at Glaneirw had coalesced and, as a newly-formed housing co-operative, was given first option to buy at cost price. The Glaneirw Housing Co-operative raised £57,000 to buy the property and start again. The deeds were split in order that a £26,000 mortgage on the land from the Ecology Building Society and a £10,000 mortgage on the house from the bank could be obtained. The remaining amount was raised from members' capital, and generous loans from ex-members, other communities and friends.

The need to service these debts launched the Glaneirw community into a new era. The co-operative has continued as a commune, income sharing but with the stipulation that each member undertakes to earn £1,300 a year as a minimum; that is, £25 per week. This has enforced a new discipline and made members devise new strategies for earning money. The most notable development has been the setting up of a business partnership between four of the members, Tivyside Heating Services. They install and modify solid fuel heaters, mainly Rayburns, with a back boiler system that enables them to provide hot water and cooking facilities and heat a bank of radiators. Other members continue with the pottery and with farming. The result is increased specialization, but there is, at the same time, a great deal of inter-change in the work. At harvest time the whole community is likely to be in the fields; if there is a rush on orders for central heating installation more help will be called on in that area. This flexibility is one of the main advantages of the income-sharing arrangement in the commune, but it does have its disadvantages. Pete West, one of the longest-standing members at Glaneirw, explained:

Whatever people earn from the farm, from the pottery, or from our plumbing business is put into the common pool and administered by the treasurer, whom we elect once a year. This gives us tremendous flexibility but also imposes enormous restraints. The flexibility comes with things like child care. I can ask someone to look after my two-year-old daughter Ceri if I have to go out on a plumbing job. Or if I feel like it I can do some cooking and no

one's going to be upset if I'm not out earning money. It allows a great mixing of work. But you have to be very trusting with each other and have a firm structure. In the past we had no guidelines and some people didn't put in as much as others and this generated a lot of bad feeling. That's one thing we've learned. We've got to be disciplined — mainly self-disciplined — in order to achieve our aims.

The community is organized by regular weekly meetings where the workload is shared out, timetables set, and problems discussed. Undoubtedly, however, it is the discipline enforced by the need to service a relatively large mortgage that has provided the impetus for the community since it was reconstituted. But every phase in a community's life brings fresh problems. By 1984 at Glaneirw, although the demands of working continued to exert most pressure, the community had achieved a sense of continuity and stability. As a

A great advantage of living co-operatively is sharing the children. Here Pete West is seen with the younger members of the Glaneirw House Community.

result individual members began to think of their own personal time and space a little more and found themselves restricted by financial pressures. Very simply, until that point no member could be allowed more than £3 a week pocket money if the books were to be balanced. As Pete, again, explained:

> All our income goes first into the community and usually the decision has been to spend the bulk of it on communal assets: so we've got a tractor, we've got central heating, we've got a new car, we've improved the house, and we've spent a lot of money on the farm. The end result has been very little left to spend on personal things to allow us some of the advantages that people in ordinary society can have — holidays and things like that. We're now reaching the stage, I think, where we need to allow more money for ourselves as individuals, perhaps £8 rather than £3 a week.

The Rainbow Housing Co-operative

The Rainbow Housing Co-operative in Milton Keynes is a much less intense form of community living than Glaneirw House, but perhaps more appropriate for an urban setting and certainly a more immediate model for most people. Comprising 33 adults and 12 children in a street of 24 renovated railway cottages, it is a kind of half-way house to a commune. Each household is financially independent — most of the residents work in conventional jobs in Milton Keynes, some at the Open University — but they come together to share a range of facilities and responsibilities in common. The most immediate impression is the fact that the gardens at the rear of the cottages have been formed into one unit, creating an open space used by the children to play in and by their parents to cultivate. More than an acre has been developed into a productive smallholding with vegetable plots, fruit bushes, chickens, ducks and bees.

Begun in June 1977 the Rainbow Co-operative set out to gain the backing of the Milton Keynes Development Corporation to renovate the old railway workers' cottages, originally built around 1850. Dilapidated and near to total ruin, they were disliked by many because their stark and rigid line and construction was all too reminiscent of the class conscious Victorian way of living. This, coupled with the fact that the sight of the tumble-down homes was regarded as an eyesore, led many local people to campaign for their demolition. But the Co-operative, formed by a small group centred at the Open University — among them Godfrey Boyle, one time editor of *Undercurrents,* the alternative technology magazine — managed to persuade the Development Corporation, and later the Borough of Milton Keynes, to back their scheme. Funded by the Corporation, the renovation costs, £200,000 at 1977 prices, produced 24

up-to-date well-equipped homes that still retain their character — in contrast to the harsh modern red-brick flats built alongside. The street itself has been given a village atmosphere by being shut off to traffic and landscaped with trees and shrubs.

Rainbow is a management co-operative. Its members collectively rent the properties from the council but have taken over their own management — that is, collecting rents, allocating tenancies, keeping accounts and general administration — for maintenance of the properties and for general upkeep of the land that goes with them. The monthly rent (1984 figures) is £68.50 for the two-bedroomed cottages, and £72 for the handful that have four bedrooms. But 40 per cent of this total is returned to the co-operative as a whole in exchange for its work in managing and maintaining the properties. This money is continuously ploughed back into the community. It pays for the materials the maintenance team uses and for the equipment and gardening materials of the land team. It has also paid for a great deal of capital equipment during the six years of Rainbow's existence: a rotovator, tools, children's play equipment, greenhouse, chicken sheds, photocopier, freezer, and a baby alarm system that links all the houses.

The money also pays the rent of one of the 24 houses which is used as a Community House. This contains a launderette, with industrial washing and drying machines, a well-equipped workshop, office and a meeting room. Here the co-operative holds its monthly meetings, attended generally by between twenty and thirty of the residents. This apportions work between the three groups that run the co-operative — the maintenance, administrative and land groups — deals with day to day problems, and selects new co-operative members when new tenancies arise. There is no formal structure requiring people to join particular groups or to undertake a set amount of work. It is left to the members to gravitate towards the group they feel suits them best and then decide on the level of their contribution. Potentially, herein lies the source of most tensions within the co-operative. For instance, the maintenance group consisted of just seven members when we visited the co-operative. Major structural repairs are the responsibility of the council, but the group replaces slates, tends to leaking guttering, and maintains the exterior decoration of all the houses and sometimes some of the interior work as well, depending on the circumstances. The co-ordinator of the maintenance group, Hugh Ross, conceded that there were problems in ensuring everyone made a fair contribution to the co-operative:

> Some people don't actually belong to one of the three groups but sort of volunteer when pressure is building up in a particular area. It is true that some members are not constantly and directly involved. But there's no real

Opposite: *Before and after.* Inset: *the terrace of railway cottages, seen in the mid-1970s prior to their renovation by the Milton Keynes Development Corporation to form today's Rainbow Community.*

way of making sure that everybody does their fair share.

In practice, the relatively small size of the co-operative, with everybody knowing each other well, has had the result of avoiding major difficulties in this area. Although Rainbow is not an income-sharing co-operative, in practice many of the members live in quite a collective way: for instance, most will participate in shared meals at least several times a week and often more, and there is a great deal of shared childcare. The Community House is a focus, too, of a great deal of social activity, regular parties and a weekly music evening presented by the Rainbow Folk group, a combination of varying instruments and varying skills. Decisions at meetings are deliberately reached by consensus, but this is an evolving process and never more so than in the choosing of new members, as the co-ordinator of the administrative group, Alan Francis, explained:

> This is one of the trickier areas and over the six years we've been here we've changed our policy several times. Now we don't just go on criteria such as position on a list or anything — that's just one of a number of factors we take into account. As well as their position on the list and their housing need we take more into account applicants' commitment to the co-operative way of living, whether they express an interest in joining one of our groups, and whether we think they'll participate in meetings and meals and so on. The whole community is involved in making the decision. We have a form of straw voting where we eliminate people until we are left with perhaps two or three households applying to join. Then it's a matter of just talking it through, quite often late into the night, until we come to a decision everyone is happy with.

Laurieston Hall

Procedures for choosing new members present a challenge to all communities, but particularly to those which have a more fully developed communal structure than the Rainbow Co-operative. It is a key test for the ideal of consensual decision-making. Of all the communes in Britain, the Laurieston Hall Community at Castle Douglas, Kirkcudbrightshire in Scotland, has perhaps the most fully worked out system. The commune has a stable membership of around ten adults and eight children, but occasionally seeks new members. It describes itself as having 'Green, Anarchist and Feminist leanings':

> We eat a mixed diet. Our aims are to develop as individuals and as a group, harmoniously: to develop our political and personal lives with respect for our local environment and with the wider society.

A prospective member of Laurieston Hall first has to get to know everyone, which may take anything from a couple of short visits to an extended stay. They can then ask to stay for a trial period, usually between six weeks and three months. Each member has a responsibility to say at that stage if they have any reservations or objections, so that no one comes for a trial unless there is a reasonable likelihood of their joining at the end of it. During this period the person takes a full part in everything going on in the community which, because it acts as a conference centre running a range of courses, can be quite hectic, especially during the summer months. The prospective member shares income and has a full voice in all decisions.

There then comes the joining meeting, which is highly structured and takes a whole morning, with everyone present. First the prospective member talks for ten minutes or so about their general feelings -- what they would contribute to the community, what their needs are, how these might or might not be met, and any changes they would like to see. This is followed by a few minutes of silent reflection. The person then spends time talking to each existing member in turn about their relationship, worries about living with each other, and problems they can envisage arising. It takes about an hour to go round the whole group in this way and there follows a break for tea. The prospective member then adds anything that may have been forgotten, before leaving the group to reach a verdict.

Anyone has the right to say No and stop a person joining, which does occasionally happen. More often, doubts are expressed which may be dissolved by further discussion and by other people's enthusiasm. There may be anger at the negative feelings of one or two people by others who want the person to join. A No answer is often followed by a post-mortem on how the process was allowed to come so far before objection was expressed. If, as most often happens, the person is accepted, the whole group takes the opportunity to celebrate. The analogy must be with the celebration that accompanies marriage.

This account of the Laurieston Hall Community's procedures for selecting new members, given in *The Collective Housing Handbook* it has published, is notable for two reasons. Firstly, it illustrates the way meetings in communities have evolved and, secondly, it illustrates the attention that communities are now giving to conflict resolution. On the first point, as the *Handbook* remarks:

> Over the last decade or so the style of meetings has changed. First there was a straightforward revolt against the authoritarian, hierarchic, usually male-dominated style of meeting — replaced by a more *laissez-faire*, 'as the spirit moves' approach. This assumed that, given the removal of constraint,

everyone was equally able to participate: equally confident, skilled, tough and experienced.

There had to be another revolt — against the tyranny of structurelessness, which allowed the most forceful cliques to dominate, and failed to confront socialized roles of submission and domination. Such meetings also failed to get the job done: they were often inefficient, timewasting and confused.

Recently, arising particularly out of the women's movement, a lot of attention has been paid to developing techniques and structures around goals of: equal power; equal responsibility; equal knowledge; and equal opportunity to participate.

Laurieston Hall's *Handbook* has an important section on conflict resolution, which it sees as a creative process:

> Conflict is a natural occurrence and will always be with us. Our task is to learn to respond to conflicts in the most creative ways possible. Conflict is an integral part of the change process. Conflict is one way that communitites and individuals grow. It is a process in which different viewpoints or actions struggle with each other, are merged, and form new ideas of human behaviour.

One of the most attractive features of the Rainbow Community is the way it has dispensed with garden fences. It gives the children plenty of open space to play in.

There follow detailed recommendations and techniques for dealing with the inevitable stress and tensions that accompany community living, under headings such as 'Negotiation and Bargaining'; 'Expressing and Hearing Feelings'; and 'Building Trust and Care'. The importance of meetings and decision-making in communitites, and resolving the conflicts that inevitably accompany them, was emphasized by Chris Mattingly, a member of the Lifespan commune at Townhead, near Sheffield:

> The means by which everyone in a community takes part in making decisions becomes an exercise in power-sharing which goes far beyond any other experiments in democracy. Community people become expert in meetings technique, in working for consensus, in accepting others as equals. These talents they take with them into the wider world and use for the benefit of others, through pressure groups, political initiatives, support organizations and all sorts of community activity. Most of the communities I know are intensely involved in local and national affairs.

By building anti-hierarchical decision-making structures along these lines the communities that form part of the Alternative Movement are making a definite political statement, though many of their members would not necessarily understand it as such. There is another important sense, too, in which these communitites, merely by existing in the way they do, are beaming a political message to society generally and that is in their attitutde to work. Chris Mattingley put the point succinctly:

> Living in any community involves work, often hard physical work or boring routine tasks. Possibly the greatest problem with people coming into communities is that they are confused about the difference between work and employment. For me, work is the activity required for my survival, that of my dependants and that of the environment which I tend. I hope that I shall enjoy this work for most of my life and make it a gift to others. When I must trade my time for money I am alienated because I make things I cannot use. If I am not careful I find myself, as an employee, contributing to the destruction of our environment through war or exploitation. In my community, I work within my chosen ethic and thus I enjoy doing as much work as I can, trusting that what I make will give life and joy to others and that the act of making will not harm me or anyone else.

Such perspectives are, ultimately, revolutionary in their implications, though the method of the communes, like so much else in the Alternative Movement, is — through example — to stimulate evolutionary change. Few outside the communities we looked at, however, would doubt the opportunities they provide for children and for the load-sharing facilities communes offer parents. As Jeannie Averill, who lives at the Glaneirw House Commune, told us:

> Pete and I have Ceri who is nearly two and we're expecting another. We share looking after Ceri equally between us and, of course, as with the other two children here, everybody is involved in bringing them up. This to me is the most positive thing about living in a commune really. I've never had children outside a communtiy like this but it strikes me as the most natural way to bring up children. In most societies over thousands of years people have always had their children in groups, either extended families or tribes. People in this situation are able to hand their child to someone else if they need to go off and do some work. And being in this position myself I can say that I've had just about zero frustrations in bringing up Ceri. But if I wasn't here, if I was in a more conventional situation in a semi-detached somewhere with a husband out at work, I'm sure I'd be irritable, bad-tempered, probably impossible to live with.

Mention of children in the context of communal living inevitably broaches the subject of the sexual relationships and motivations of those who live in them. The short answer to such queries is that this appears the one area of communal living that is most similar to life in conventional society. A rather longer answer was given us by Pete West:

> One thing I've actually found is that people who form relationships in a communal setting are often more stable in them because they've got to know each other well beforehand without any pressure. In conventional society it tends to be that you meet someone at a dance and maybe you have sex with them. And then I bet you get quite involved before you really know that person. But living with a group of people you can really take your time to get to know someone's personality. And if you really think about it, if you're actually living with people for years on end you just can't go round sleeping with each other. The emotions involved would be so strong and so much jealousy would be aroused that you'd just never survive.

The communal movement of the 1980s is much more about survival and rather less optimistic than the movement of 1960s. But the important thing about it is that it still exists — and exists, moreover, after having experienced adversity, often emotional turmoil, and certainly, at times, hardship. The communes and co-operatives of the 1980s are tougher than their forbears. There is less of a feel of excitement and expansion about them, but they are more stable and more likely to survive to carry forward their message of an entirely holistic approach to alternative living. And there remains a craving for the kind of lifestyle they represent. Their magazines and publications remain full of advertisements from individuals — often single mothers with children — groups, and couples seeking a new start in a communal setting. Witness the following that appeared in the Communes Network newsletter in December 1983:

> We three (couple in mid-30s and two-year-old boy . . . with another on the way) would like to meet other people with young children who might be interested in property-sharing and co-operative living in mid-Wales. The kind of set-up which would come near to our ideal would be to live next door or near to other compatible families — or else co-purchase and split up a big house with land so that people would not be living communally but would share spaces and facilities such as a garden, workshops, laundry, play areas etc. Helping each other would be the essence.
>
> Many people, happily, evolve this sort of relationship with their neighbours without having to contrive it; but for most escapees from the city, buying a house in an unfamiliar area involves so much luck as to what sort of community (or lack of it) one 'lands' in. We've always made friends wherever we've lived but our present situation of nuclear isolation in a tiny north Wales hamlet means that to keep our young son and us in contact with friends we have to drive many miles each week, which seems equally artificial.
>
> We're vegetarian, socialist in outlook, play musical instruments, love traditional folk music, and one of us is learning Welsh. We're keen to get off the dole into self-employment. . .

Left: The Rainbow Community is a housing co-operative not a commune, so there is a limit on how much is shared in common. Each family is self-sufficient but many come together in the Community House to share meals and thrash out common decisions on a consensus basis.

Below: Forty per cent of the rent paid by the members of the Co-operative is returned to them because they manage the properties themselves. It goes towards community facilities like this well-equipped workshop.

Source Guide

All the communities we have looked at we would define as sharing the values of the Alternative Movement, as outlined in our opening chapter. For a list of such communities *Communes Network* magazine has published a directory; both this and the bi-monthly magazine (current subscription £4 for ten issues) are available from Some People in Leicester Community, 89 Evington Road, Leicester LE2 1QH.

There is an International Communes Network that links communities throughout the world and produces its own magazine: contact Laurieston Hall, Laurieston, Castle Douglas, Kirkcudbrightshire, Scotland. You can obtain from the same address *The Collective Housing Handbook* by Sarah Eno and Dave Treanor, which is essential reading for anyone interested in the practical problems (legal frameworks, finance, accounting, and tax questions, as well the more human issues of income sharing and conflict resolution) of community living. The book also contains a comprehensive list of contacts and useful addresses.

There are some communities we have come across that we would not class as being within the ambit of the Alternative Movement as we have defined it. Perhaps the most notable is 'The Teachers', a group of 14 adults and 9 children, based at 18 Garth Road, Bangor, Gwynedd. They describe themselves as a 'dedicated rationalist teaching order' and operate under a complex system of rules involving a distinctly hierachical and authoritarian approach. They have published a range of pamphlets on their philosophy and also an Alternative Communities Directory which, now running into a fourth edition, contains a comprehensive survey of the whole, very wide, range of communities in Britain.

There is a lack of up-to-date books dealing with communal living, a reflection perhaps of the waning of the movement as the recession gathered pace in the late 1970s and early 1980s. But there are signs of awakening interest by publishers. Meanwhile, probably the best sociological background has been provided in American-authored books produced in the 1970s: for example *Commitment and Community: Communes and Utopias in Sociological Perspective* by R. M. Kantar (Harvard University Press, 1972). A perspective British study is *Communes, Sociology and Society* by P. Abrams and A. McCulloch (Cambridge University Press, 1976). *Communes in Britain* by Andrew Rigby (Routledge and Kegan Paul, 1974), although somewhat dated, contains useful portraits of five communitites active at that time.

WWOOF (Working Weekends on Organic Farms) is a non-profit making exchange scheme whereby bed and board are given in return for help in communities, organic farms and smallholdings throughout Britain. A very useful way of gaining a taste of communal living and 'back to the land' lifestyle, relatively painlessly. For information and a brochure send a stamped addressed envelope to: WWOOF, 19 Bradford Road, Lewes, East Sussex BN7 1RB.

6
THE
NEW AGE

Our vision is of the earth as an organism within ever greater organisms, and the whole alive. Everything is ultimately spirit, in different conditions of density. Space exploration in our age need not only be by rocket; it can also be through lifted consciousness . . .

Sir George Trevelyan

The New Age has no organization and no leaders. It is about a very broad transformation in values and ways of looking at the world. All the people and activities described in this book can be seen as part of the New Age movement. Terminology can, of course, be divisive. Some would hesitate to subscribe to the idea of a New Age for fear of participating in some kind of new religious dogma. They might prefer to use alternative expressions like Aquarian Age, Consciousness Age, or Solar Age. Yet all these expressions refer to the latter part of the twentieth century as marking the beginning of a significant shift or turning point in values and awareness. All would accept a definition of the shift as being from a mechanistic view of the world to a holistic view. All would be willing to place their values firmly within an ecological context that sees the person and the planet as part of the same unified whole.

This idea of seeing humanity and environment as a single system, which is so fundamental to the New Age, arises out of a rejection of the Cartesian scientific perspective that has dominated thinking since the sixteenth century. As we noted in our chapter on healing, Descartes' celebrated statement 'Cogito, ergo sum' — I think, therefore I exist — encouraged Western individuals to equate their identity with their rational mind rather than with their whole organism. This led to a division of mind and matter, to dualism, which in turn developed a mechanistic view of the universe. Matter was thought to be the basis of all existence, and the material world was seen as a multitude of separate objects assembled into a huge machine. Scientific method then became a question of dividing things up and breaking things down into their separate building blocks so they could be studied.

But in the twentieth century it is science itself, and particularly physics, that has demonstrated the limitations and inaccuracies of the mechanistic world view. The ultimate building blocks of matter were thought to be atoms; but physics has now shown that far from being hard, solid particles, atoms consist of neutrons and electrons and these in turn have been demonstrated to be energy waves. These ideas have been extensively explored by Fritjof Capra, a physicist who has also studied Eastern philosphy, in his seminal book for New Age thinking *The Turning Point.* In it he states that, in contrast to the mechanistic Cartesian view of the world, the world view emerging from modern physics can

Previous page: Holistic astrologer Errol Masters with some of his signs of the Zodiac. We are, he says, in the transition period towards the dawning of the Age of Aquarius at the end of the century: truly a New Age following the conflicts of the Piscean era of the last 2,000 years.

be characterized by words like organic, holistic and ecological: 'The universe is no longer seen as a machine, made up of a multitude of objects, but has to be pictured as one indivisible, dynamic whole whose parts are essentially interrelated and can be understood only as patterns of a cosmic process.'

In essence, too, this statement describes astrology's Cosmic Law, otherwise known as the Law of Correspondence or Law of Holism. Quite simply it states that since everything is interrelated and contained within ever expanding wholes — as atoms within molecules, molecules within cells and so on up to the planetary system and beyond — this explains how the movement of the planets can influence our behaviour. In the context of the New Age, however, the astrological significance is the astrologer's claim that we are currently moving into a new era, that we are progressing through a turbulent period of transition into the Age of Aquarius that will dawn towards the end of the century. Astrologers characterize Aquarius as an age of increasing harmony, high moral idealism and spiritual growth, in stark contrast to the Age of Pisces that precedes it. A holistic astrologer we interviewed, Errol Masters, explained the transition as follows:

> If you consider the great solar year in which the sun travels through the 12 zodiacal constellations, it takes 25,868 years exactly. If we then divide that year up into its solar months, it works out to about 2,100 years per cycle. These are called the astrological ages, so that when the sun is travelling through these ages we have whole new civilizations and cultures emerging in our planet.
>
> The last 2,000 years have been the Piscean age which was initiated by Jesus and the Christian teachings. This is now coming to an end and the new age of Aquarius is about to unfold itself. These ages determine ways of living, culture, civilization, and religions.
>
> So Pisces was a very sacrificial age. Its keynote was sacrifice, as we can see if we look at the Christian saints and martyrs. It was also an age of duality, of polarization in which everything split in two directions — hence the Piscean symbol of two fishes swimming in opposite directions. Over the last 2,000 years we've had polarization between cultures, between civilizations, between religions, between black and white.
>
> In contrast the age of Aquarius is completely different. Its keynotes are unity and diversity, co-operation and a global consciousness which will replace the old separation of consciousness which typified the Piscean age.

The idea of consciousness, and an expanding all-enveloping consciousness at that, is central to the New Age. So much so that Peter Russell, an author who has done more than most to popularize the spiritual perspective of the

Alternative Movement, refers to the New Age as the Consciousness Age. What is being talked about is not at all new. The inner tranquillity and strength that come from an awareness of oneness with the planet and the whole of creation has been experienced by mystics down the ages. What the New Age demands is that the experience be shared by the whole of humanity and so effect the necessary transformation into Aquarian values. In his book *The Awakening Earth* Russell distils the teaching of a phalanx of sages and gurus into the sentence 'Our individual consciousnesses are like drops of water taken from an ocean: each drop is a unique individual drop, with its own particular qualities and identity; yet each drop is also of the same essence as the ocean — water.' And he quotes Edward Carpentier, the nineteenth-century social scientist and poet who wrote:

> If you inhabit thought (and persevere) you come at length to a region of consciousness below or behind thought . . . and a realization of an altogether vaster self than that to which we are accustomed. And since the ordinary consciousness, with which we are concerned in daily life, is before all things founded on the little local self . . . it follows that to pass out of that is to die to the ordinary self and the ordinary world.
>
> It is to die in the ordinary sense, but in another, it is to wake up and find that the 'I', one's real, most intimate self, pervades the Universe and all other beings — that the mountains and the sea and the stars are a part of one's body and that one's soul is in touch with the souls of all creatures.

Russell sees the development of consciousness as the next evolutionary step

Hazel Henderson's presentation of the phases in human development, culminating in the Solar Age.

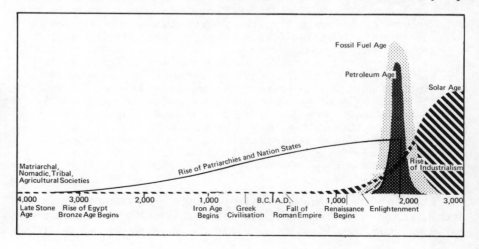

humanity must take if it is to survive. The first major evolutionary leap humanity made, the one that distinguishes it from other creatures, was to self-reflective consciousness. This enabled us not only to be aware of ourselves as conscious thinking beings but to become conscious of the essence of consciousness itself, the pure Self:

> The urge that many people feel to grow and develop inwardly is nothing less than the force of evolution manifesting within our own consciousness. It is the Universe evolving through us.

The challenge is to find means of promoting this inner evolution on a wide, planetary scale, and in time to combat the more destructive impulses of human nature. Russell, perhaps over-optimistically, sees an exponential growth under way in the numbers of people and organizations active in the field of inner transformation. We are more familiar with the idea of exponential growth — that is, activity doubling and doubling again over set periods of time — in the field of information technology: for instance, the fantastic proliferation of computers and computer technology. Russell is predicting a similar trend in the explosion of consciousness, whose development, he predicts, will outstrip the exponential growth of information technology somewhere around the year 2000: hence the idea of the Age of Consciousness.

For those who find definition of the New Age in terms of Aquarian timescale and values, or of the expansion of inner consciousness, somewhat fanciful, explanation in terms of the Solar Age should appear more pragmatic. The coming of the Solar Age has been most associated within the Alternative Movement with Hazel Henderson, the American economist and futurologist. Her starting point is that the Solar Age is emerging out of the transition from our dependence on coal, gas and oil. The Fossil Fuel Age began in the early 1700s in England, will peak sometime around the year 2100 and be exhausted around 2300. Even though our society is caught somewhere in the middle, historically, of the Fossil Fuel Age (see diagram), the transition from society living on the earth's stored fossil fuel 'capital' to solar driven energy is already under way. Some of the methods of harnessing renewable solar-driven energy were examined in Chapter 2. Henderson's substantive point, however, is that this underlying energy transition will have major consequences for the structure of industrialized society. She points to a law of diminishing returns affecting industrial expansion, with Western societies in particular hitting an 'inexorable energy crunch' coupled with bureaucratic bottlenecks. When, under these pressures, industrial economies reach a certain limit of centralized, capital-intensive production, they *have to shift direction*, to more decentralized

Peter Russell's projected growth curve of the proportion of the population working in the field of inner development (the 'Consciousness Curve'). Although small in numbers at present, if the current rapid rate of growth is sustained, he predicts the number of people working in this area will eventually overtake the information curve.

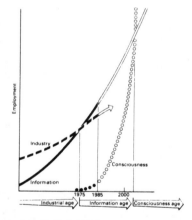

111

economic activities and political frameworks:

> This change of direction is a scenario for 'spontaneous devolution', where citizens begin simply recalling the power they once delegated to politicians, administrators and bureaucrats, and the power they delegated to business leaders to make far-reaching technological decisions. The growth in all mature industrial countries of citizen movements for consumer and environmental protection, corporate and government accountability, human rights and social justice; the drive for worker self-management; the growth of the human potential movement, self-help care; 'small is beautiful' technologies; alternative lifestyles; and the rise of ethnic pride and indigenous peoples, as well as the tax revolt, are all parts of this 'spontaneous devolution' of old, unsustainable structures.

Whatever perspective is taken on the New Age — whether astrological, mystical, or politico-economic — all its exponents start with a holistic ecological vision. We opened this chapter with a discussion of the twentieth century's rejection of the dualistic, mechanistic systems of thought that dominated the previous three or four centuries, when mind and body tended to be split into two. It is, then, extraordinarily apt that research since the mid-1960s into the workings of the brain has discovered that it is split into left and right sides that specialize in different types of activity. The left hemisphere tends to operate (in a right-handed person, at least) in a linear mode. It tends, in other words, to deal with ideas one after the other, and so is prone to divide them up into separate entities. Consequently it is ideally suited to coping with language. The right side of the brain is more concerned with visual-spatial functions, aesthetic and emotional appreciation, and with intuitive thought. It is tempting to say, further, that the left-hand side of the brain, the guardian of focused consciousness, represents a masculine dominated perspective; whereas the right-hand side reflects a feminine approach. Certainly, the left is more analytic, moving in a step-by-step fashion, while the right is more synthetic, processing more holistically.

What is generally true, as well, is that the left-hand side of the brain is dominant in our culture, issuing a continuing stream of linguistic, rational analysis and instruction. It tends to be out-of-touch with the right-hand side whose more reflective, intuitive consciousness is suppressed. A New Age principle is that the effort must be made to bring the two into balance. For as Fritjof Capra puts it, rational left-hand brain thinking is linear, whereas ecological awareness arises from an intuition of nonlinear systems:

> One of the most difficult things for people in our culture to understand is the

fact that if you do something that is good, then more of the same will not necessarily be better. This, to me, is the essence of ecological thinking. Ecosystems sustain themselves in a dynamic balance based on cycles and fluctuations, which are nonlinear processes. Linear entreprises, such as indefinite economic and technological growth — or, to give a more specific example, the storage of radioactive waste over enormous time spans — will necessarily interfere with the natural balance and, sooner or later, will cause severe damage.

Can it be that the sprawling urban and industrial development of our cities can be viewed as a kind of planetary cancer?

The Gaia Hypothesis

The apotheosis of the holistic ecological approach, so symptomatic of the Alternative Movement, is the idea that the earth itself should be regarded as a single living organism. Interestingly enough this idea, known as the Gaia hypothesis, after the Greek goddess of the earth, developed out of the space programme of the 1960s. The first astronauts were able, for the first time in human history, to look at the planet from outer space. Their perception of the planet in all its shining beauty — a blue and white globe floating in the deep darkness of space — was, as many of them have declared since, a profound spiritual experience. The pictures of the 'Whole Earth' they brought back with them became a powerful new symbol for the ecology movement. A British chemist, James Lovelock, who in the early 1960s worked at the California Institute of Technology on space-related programmes, developed a comprehensive theory in his *Gaia: A New Look at Life on Earth*. This is a detailed study of the ways in which the biosphere seems to keep the chemical composition of the air, the temperature on the surface of the earth, and many other aspects, at the optimum levels to sustain life as we know it. Thus, for instance, the stabilization of the oxygen concentration in the atmosphere at 21 per cent is just the right level for the maintenance of life. A few per cent less and the larger animals and flying insects could not have found enough energy to survive; a few per cent more and even wet vegetation would burn well.

There is not the space here to describe further the Gaia hypothesis, fascinating though it is. The main point is that it provides a perfect context for the holistic ecological approach that is the quintessence of the New Age. Moreover, one strand of New Age thinking at least has charted an ambitious, even exotic, role for humanity within Gaia. This is for it to act, as Peter Russell puts it in the subtitle to his book, as some kind of 'global brain'. But as he told us:

> There are several possibilities. Taken together humanity is reaching the stage on the planet where it is becoming analogous to the human brain. The way we are joining ourselves up with telephones, computers, and satellites, exchanging information and storing it in libraries, we are developing into some gigantic planetary nervous system.
>
> But if we are a nervous system, we are also one which appears to be rather malignant at the moment. In some respects we are rather like a planetary cancer. It's interesting that if you look at a city from the air, it looks very much like the way a cancer grows into the body. And if you go deeper into what happens with cancer, it's that individual cells become rogue cells, selfish cells, doing their own thing at the expense of the system.
>
> Basically, this is just what much of humanity does. We have become so separated in our minds from the rest of the environment that we think we

can look after ourselves to the detriment of the environment. But we are beginning to learn that it doesn't work, that, for instance, decimating our equatorial rain forests is just increasing the carbon dioxide build-up in the atmosphere, which may trigger an ice age in ten years' time.

What New Age thinking is saying is that we must learn how to co-operate as a species with each other and with the environment. The question is, can we shift from a very selfish, petty, competitive mode of functioning to a much more co-operative holistic mode of working with each other and with nature? Unless we do, we will probably wipe ourselves out in ten or twenty years' time. I think humanity is now coming up against its final evolutionary exam.

What unites the great variety of people and activities we have looked at in this book is that they are all seeking a 'co-operative holistic mode of working'. In different ways, too, they are all seeking to change their lifestyle to blend more ecologically with the planet, with Gaia. So it is not surprising that so many of the people we met in the Alternative Movement are vegetarian. The starting point, usually, is that protein production from animals is highly inefficient and in global terms is undermining efforts to overcome the food and energy crisis affecting much of the Third World. Secondly, meat, which provides about one-third of the fat intake of the average person in Britain, is generally regarded as a less healthy diet source than vegetables, cereals and fruits. But beyond these pragmatic considerations, killing animals and eating 'dead flesh' appears to those who have fully absorbed the 'holistic world view' to contradict the essential oneness of life on the planet. The relationship between plants and animals (including humans) is, in contrast, seen as mutually supportive and holistic. Animal survival through the eating of plants is necessary for the survival of the plants as a whole as well. It is an example of co-operation which secures, for instance, the distribution and circulation of oxygen and carbon dioxide in a rhythmic movement that makes life possible.

Feminine Awareness

The second most striking feature common to the variety of people we have met in researching this book is the emphasis given to the role and contribution of women. There is a conscious recognition by both women and men within the Alternative Movement that a new balance must be found between the masculine and feminine impulses. This is analagous to the search discussed earlier for a new balance between the consciousness of the left-hand and right-hand brain hemispheres. Fritjof Capra, as usual, has expressed the theory very well:

The spiritual essence of the ecological vision seems to find its ideal expression in the feminist spirituality advocated by the women's movement, as would be expected from the natural kinship between feminism and ecology, rooted in the age-old identification of women and nature. Feminist spirituality is based on awareness of the oneness of all living forms and of their cyclical rhythms of birth and death, thus reflecting an attitude towards life that is profoundly ecological. . .

Throughout Britain today groups of women are springing up that, through organizing support services for other women and campaigning on a broad political front, are projecting the New Age ecological vision more vigorously than any other initiative. We spoke to one such group, at the Greenhouse networking centre in Bangor. They began by emphasizing that the women's movement, like

Spokespeople of the Feminist movement being interviewed. They have no formal organization and no leaders. They see themselves in the vanguard of the New Age.

the New Age movement as a whole, is anti-hierarchical and without leaders:

> We are without hierarchy, which is something different from the average organization. We are not like CND, for instance, which has someone you can recognize at its head. A great example of how we work is the Greenham Women's Peace Camp. Any woman can go to Greenham and become a Greenham woman. There aren't identifiable women who form the camp so that if they leave it falls apart. This approach is one of the unique things about the women's movement and something that's moving into the New Age kind of thinking. . .
>
> Something common to both the Women's and the New Age movements is a responsibility to the self and to the others who work with you. You can't have cooperation without both aspects. So in the Women's movement we don't have general policy statements. We tend to try and work as individuals and to understand ourselves as women. . .
>
> The masculine/feminine imbalance is something talked about a lot in terms of the New Age and, of course, we would like to see a better balance. But we don't want to see it within the structure we already have. We can think about creating opportunities for women, but they mustn't be the same opportunities as already exist for men. We need a whole different outlook. . .
>
> Women can get strong and whole but in the present context there are still places we can't go and times of the day when it is not safe for us to walk around. So in a fundamental sense, despite changes that have taken place, women's personal safety and freedom are still restricted. It's everything that actually needs to shift, not just the women. . .

So the women's movement is as much to do with men as women themselves, which is very much a New Age response. As Fritjof Capra, again, puts it: 'One of the most radical contributions men can make to developing our collective feminist awareness will be to get fully involved in raising our children from the moment of birth, so that they can grow up with the experience of the full human potential inherent in women and men.' Pete West at the Glaneirw House commune we profiled in the previous chapter shares the upbringing of his two-year-old daughter, Ceri, with her mother Jeannie Averill. Each looks after her for generally half of every day. Pete freely declares an ideological motivation but says the lifestyle has brought practical benefits as well:

> I think it is one of the fundamental things wrong with our society that the male and female roles are so split that men and women can't basically understand one another. By actually taking care of a child on a planned long-term basis, which is traditionally women's work, I can gain a fuller appreciation of women's position and outlook. That actually makes me feel a lot closer to women generally.

Work

Parallel with the holistic perspective on balancing the feminine and masculine impulses and sharing the upbringing of children is a holistic approach to work, another New Age principle. This is tied in closely to the feminist question, since work is traditionally identified with a cleavage between the male leaving the home to employment elsewhere and the female staying at home to concentrate on domestic tasks. The holistic New Age attitude is to arrange things so that the traditional male/female division of labour is shared and focused on the home. This is one of the more challenging aspects of the New Age prescriptions for co-operative living, since if applied on a wide scale it would mean a revolutionary change in the way industry is organized. Consequently, there is unlikely to be revolutionary change in this direction. Rather, like the rest of New Age thinking, there is likely to be evolutionary change in the direction being advocated. In this case new technology, the development of more sophisticated communication links such as cable television and home computer terminals, will aid the evolutionary process. More and more work, now typically carried out in offices, will be able to be undertaken at home. The benefits in human terms, as with the sharing of child care, are plain to see. The editors of *Resurgence* magazine, Satish Kumar and June Mitchell, have consciously developed a work-sharing approach to the job and the upbringing of their family, as June explained:

> Having work and the home shared and in one place enabled me to avoid many of the frustrations and decisions that afflict, I suppose, most women. For instance, there is the difficult choice women face of choosing to make a career or have children. I was able to say I could do both. We took on *Resurgence* when my eldest child Mukti was six months old. So I had nappies in one drawer and manuscripts for editing in another drawer of the same desk.
>
> By now the combination has grown. We have a garden and our cow, Hazel. So the children can share the garden and the cow and come into the office and stamp cheques or have a go with our little calculator. So in this way they learn how we earn our living and also the pleasures of living together. For all the time Satish is intent on pulling me into the office to help him out with proof reading or some other task, and I'm pulling him into the kitchen because we have someone for dinner and want to cook something special.
>
> The way we operate is more holistic because home and work should not be divided. The essence of holism is to have home and work united.

The American Indian Medicine Wheel

The ecological awareness that is so central to the Alternative Movement and the idea of the New Age is bound up with what can only be seen as an intuitive sense of balance in living. Such intuitive awareness is characteristic of traditional, nonliterate cultures, especially of American Indian cultures, in which life was organized around a highly refined awareness of the environment. It therefore comes as no surprise to find many people in the Alternative Movement in Britain discovering inspiration from the teachings of the American Indian Medicine Wheel. It seems at times that the American tipi has been adopted as the instantly recognizable symbol of a new British alternative lifestyle. In our opening chapter we discovered a management training centre in Anglesey, North Wales, that was in the process of adding the teachings of the Medicine Wheel to its more conventional curriculum of outward bound courses for many of British industry's high-flying managers. The source of this inspiration is forty-year-old Tim Macartney, a former drama teacher, who originally came to the management centre as its gardener. He set up home in his tipi in the garden and inevitably attracted the curiosity of managers more accustomed to multi-storey office blocks. He explained the relevance of the Medicine Wheel to twentieth-century industrialized urban society in the following terms:

> The Medicine Wheel teachings speak of the necessity for every individual to develop themselves as a whole person. They say that we are born at a certain place on the wheel of life, upon the Medicine Wheel, and there are certain qualities that are associated with these places. So a person born in the south has the qualities of trust and innocence. But if they don't also possess the qualities of the north, wisdom, then they will forever be unable to see beyond very narrow parameters. So the Medicine teachings are to tread the whole Wheel, to become a whole person. Think not as an individual, nor as a family, nor even as a nation, but think globally. In the ecological crisis of our time, thinking about the world in this sense, in a holistic sense, is the manner in which we will see ourselves into the next century.

Another tipi dweller, Nick Twilley, who lives with his wife and two small children in a community in Gloucestershire, told us that the lifestyle produced a new awareness of the elements earth, wind, fire and water:

> Living in the comfort of an ordinary house, perhaps with central heating, becomes a wall between you and the real world of nature. Step through that wall and you feel the wind, you know what it's like to be cold, you need more urgently the flickering flames of a real fire, you start to know the rain and the sun.
>
> In the tipi you experience the movement of the seasons and you are closer to the spirit world which lies in all this movement. The tipi is a fine path to tread because it is a circle of energy which is, again, a very different experience from urban life with its squares and rectangles. As energy shapes

119

these have a tendency to focus our minds in straight lines and create limited thought patterns. But with the circle there is a continuous flow of energy which is the circle or wheel of life itself.

So when you live in a tipi you are within an energy shape that is inherently nourishing. The tipi is also a cone which nourishes the life force in an additional way. So far as I remember it, living in a building and in an urban setting has a tendency to degenerate your life force. You have to work extremely hard to keep yourself feeling clean, feeling good, and feeling happy about life. Now living in a circular energy provided by the tipi, that effort evaporates — you are nourished by the nature of the shape in which you live.

Purification

Nick Twilley belongs to Prana, a loose network of, by now, about thirty people scattered throughout Britain but based near Cenarth in west Wales. Prana are best known by their chants, a melodic, intensely rhythmic, but repetitive form of singing that uses words from the American Indians, the medicine men. These distil the holistic message that is the essence of the New Age. Thus one of the Prana chants runs on, and on:

> The Earth is our Mother
> We will take care of her . . .

Another chant recites:

> Wearing my long-wing feathers as I fly
> I circle around, I circle around
> The boundaries of the earth . . .

The power is in the repetition, which stops thinking, the linear activity of the left-hand side of the brain, and allows the right-hand intuitive side of the brain to focus on sheer experience. As Prana say, 'Our music creates energy which purifies our souls and purifies the planet'. Prana originally came together to practise Re-birthing, a continuous breathing technique developed in the early 1970s by Leonard Orr in California. It works on the principle that there is a direct connection between mental and physical well-being and the openness of breathing. Continuous breathing, usually lasting one hour under the guidance of an experienced 'rebirther', has the effect of building up energy in the body. This is not dissipated physically but generates what can only be described as 'pure holistic experience', which generally produces some kind of emotional release. Mary Brooks, a member of Prana who is a practising rebirther, explained the origin of the term:

At the moment of birth one comes from a totally enclosed, secure and warm environment into the cold, bright, noisy outside world where you have to breathe. That moment is probably the most traumatic thing that ever happens to us in our lives. So, though the object of rebirthing is not necessarily to make people re-experience their birth, lots of people have done so using the technique. At the time of birth many people hold their breath or gasp for their first breath with pain. We have found that by simply linking one's breath into a rhythm of connected breathing it's possible to release a lot of mental blockages that have built up probably since birth. It's a very powerful technique; perhaps the most powerful for starting on the road to spiritual purification.

Another very basic technique of purification, this one derived directly from the American Indians, is the sweat lodge. This is an open-air sauna using a make-shift branch and twig igloo-like structure covered in blankets and heated by stones from a wood fire. The whole is prepared according to an elaborate ritual laid down by the Indians to symbolize the archetypal forces that influence our lives. Nick Twilley, who travels the country conducting workshops on Indian philosophy and techniques, sees the sweat lodge as a powerful focus for New Age transformation:

It is a place where we come together as human beings to search for the basic elements of the earth itself. We are meeting with fire, with water, with the wind. Above all we are meeting with our voices in chant and without any

Left: Prana member Nick Twilley with his wife Lena and small daughter Zoe. Living in a tipi, he says, brings you closer to the rhythm of the seasons and the spirit world — 'It is a fine path to tread'.

Right: The sweat lodge: symbol of the New Age call for inner and outer purification: 'a powerful point of change'.

121

dressing up because we are naked at that point. So it is a very simple, very basic, and very powerful point of change.

The activity of much of the New Age movement is directed at working on the personal self, in the belief that there must be a personal transformation before change can be effected within society at large. The New Age is looking very specifically at the year 2000 as a turning point for planetary consciousness. But it is equally aware that the process of change is already well under way. The 1960s are seen as the decade when the first flush of the new consciousness emerged. Astrologers are divided as to when the transition to the Age of Aquarius began but there seems to be general agreement that it was around the late 1960s, with 1967 being thought of as the most likely year the transition began. And it is perhaps no coincidence that 1967 ended with the Beatles, at the peak of their career, proclaiming 'All you need is Love'. The message was simple, in many ways self-evident. But the age-old question remained: how to put it into practice?

The question was posed in more starkly political terms at the time by the historian and CND veteran AJP Taylor who, speaking of the decline of CND in the 1960s, said: 'You have grand marches, you have meetings all over the country which show support and what do you do next? You have the same marches all over again, and you have the same meetings all over again, and you carry the same resolutions, and what do you do next? And there comes a time when people say, "We've done this" and the whole thing fades away because they couldn't think of how to do it any more.'

So it was interesting to see that by the early 1980s an answer was being found to AJP Taylor's question, and that essentially it was a New Age answer. Formulated into a slogan it read: 'Think globally — act locally'. In political terms the response came from a combination of the single-issue Green movements of the 1970s and the Peace movement of the 1960s. It was articulated in a pamphlet issued by the newly-formed Green CND in 1983 that made out the case for a holistic ecological approach to the world's problems, more fundamental than the single-issue campaigns of previous decades:

The possibility of a nuclear holocaust is a threat without parallel. Yet it is only one of the countless threats that our kind of progress now poses to the natural world. In a quite absurd way, we still see ourselves as species apart from or above the rest of creation, when we are, of course, still embedded within it. Every threat to the earth is, in fact, a threat to us; every wound inflicted on the earth is a wound against ourselves.

That understanding is totally at odds with the way we choose to live today. We cannot go on ripping up the planet as if there were no tomorrow,

Opposite: *Prana — Hindu for breath or life-force — seen here at their base in west Wales near Cardigan. Members of the group who have developed a 'New Age' philosophy based on a combination of Eastern and American Indian influences, have spread through Britain.*

desperately pursuing an illusion of economic security, regardless of the cost to the physical environment or the human spirit. Our responsibility to the planet, and to those future generations who will inherit from us, compels us to change *now* before it is too late.

The green view of peace thus poses a clear challenge to the rest of the movement. What chance is there of peace when we are all perpetually at war? At war with each other, since 'success' in today's materialistic world is possible only at someone else's cost. And at war with the planet, since today's affluence is achieved only at the expense of our natural wealth. It is in this context that the nuclear arms race is simply the most costly, most deadly, extension of a world *already at war*.

The Green, almost by definition, New Age view of peace advocates that instead of shouting 'Jobs, not Bombs' people should start setting up their own co-operatives and small businesses. In short, instead of railing against outrages and problems which can appear hopelessly large, overbearing and insoluble, you start small, on your own patch, by changing your life, your world and hence, indirectly, the world of others. Problems, said Fritz Schumacher, have become too big, too complex, and too violent :

These three features, taken together, make them incompatible with human nature, the rest of living nature, and the resource endowment of the world. If we want to help ourselves, we must work to use the fulness of our modern knowledge, consciously and with the utmost determination to create — or recreate — a technology and organizational structures which are:
— small, that is adapted to human scale;
— simple, so that we do not have to become too specialized to be wise;
— non-violent, in the sense of working with Nature instead of bludgeoning her all the time.

The Alternative Nobel Prize

In 1980 Jakob von Uexkull, a Swedish expert on rare postage stamps, sold his collection and put the proceeds into a fund devoted to recognizing alternative visionaries and ideas. It was an effort to gain more recognition and publicity for the Alternative Movement. Von Uexkull's objective was to project the idea of Right Livelihood which, as he put it, means 'living lightly — not taking more than our share of the earth's resources'. Though known officially as The Right Livelihood Award, because it is presented in Stockholm, the day before the Nobel Prize awards, it has become known as the Alternative Nobel Prize.

In 1982 one of the Alternative Nobel Prize winners was Sir George Trevelyan for his work in founding the Wrekin Trust. This aims to bring together healers and doctors, scientists and mystics to develop a common vision

Fritz Schumacher who called small 'beautiful' and with that phrase projected ecological thinking to a mass audience.

and a new, more holistic, world view. As he told us:

> Ours is the first generation to recognize that humanity is a living organism, yet we are exploiting and polluting the planet to such an extent that we threaten to destroy it. But out of holistic thinking there inevitably follows what is loosely called the alternative lifestyle, a way of living which is co-operating with the living planet rather than persisting in behaviour that threatens to destroy it.

In 1983 an Alternative Nobel Prize winner was Leopold Kohr, the Austrian apostle of the beauty in smallness and the concepts of appropriate size and technology. And as he told us:

> The confrontation of our age is not capitalism versus communism, left versus right, man versus women, black versus white, young versus old. These are issues of the past, lingering on as the glow of the sun reddens the sky after it has set. The real confrontation of our age is man versus mass, the individual versus society, the citizen versus the state, the small community versus the big one, David versus Goliath.

But it would be inappropriate in a book devoted to the Alternative Movement and its vision of a New Age to end with the views of those among it who have achieved wide recognition and who therefore threaten to become its leaders, in however informal or spiritual a sense. In our seven weeks of filming 'Alternatives', the most poignant symbol of the trust, commitment and optimism that so marks out the activists of the Alternative Movement was an ash tree planted by Tim Macartney in his garden at Cornelyn Manor on Anglesey. As he told us:

> This little tree stands at the centre of the garden. The circle that is the garden represents the universe. This tree growing in the centre of the circle represents the tree of life. Every year the garden moves round one quarter — the vegetables rotate and the garden rotates with them. In four years, time, when this garden has made one complete revolution, this little tree will be taken and planted in the east of the British Isles. On the Medicine Wheel the east represents the place of illumination and enlightenment. I will then plant another young tree here in the centre of the garden and after another four years have passed that tree will be taken to the north, the place of wisdom on the Medicine Wheel. Ultimately in the year 1999, one month before we move into the year 2000, there will stand at the four compass points of the British Isles, an ash tree, each one symbolizing life and hope for the century to come: a symbol that the New Age will occur in reality and not just as a concept or theory.

Sir George Trevelyan — a prophet of the New Age; winner of the Alternative Nobel Prize, 1982.

Source Guide

Apart from the many people we interviewed in the course of making the series 'Alternatives', we were influenced by a number of books that have appeared since the late 1970s on the emerging culture of the New Age. Most are available from the Schumacher Book Service, an arm of the Schumacher Society which exists to promote the ideas of the late Dr E. F. Schumacher. It operates from Ford House, Hartland, Bideford, Devon. Send a stamped, addressed, envelope to this address and they will return a comprehensive list of the New Age books they have in stock. We should perhaps mention a number which we have found particularly helpful in preparing this chapter: *The Turning Point* by Fritjof Capra (Fontana paperback) and *The Awakening Earth* by Peter Russell (Ark paperbacks). Both these books have comprehensive references to further reading that are an illustration in themselves of the rapidly expanding consciousness that is the essence of the New Age.

In political terms, one of us, John Osmond, published in 1978 *Creative Conflict* (Routledge and Kegan Paul) which explored ideas of decentralization, devolution and community-based politics, particularly as they relate to Wales, that have many New Age connotations. A more general source guide to New Age groups and activities in Brtain, and throughout the world, can be found in *The New Times Network,* compiled by Robert Adams (Routledge and Kegan Paul). The Foreword to this last book is written by David Spangler, a visionary, if rather impenetrable, thinker who emerged out of the extraordinary Findhorn Foundation, a community in northern Scotland that has been at the forefront of New Age development. Founded in 1962, it has by today influenced many thousands of people throughout the world, and still runs courses, seminars and conferences on New Age themes. For further information write to The Findhorn Foundation, The Park, Forres, Scotland. P. Hawken has written *The Magic of Findhorn* (Fontana, 1976).

There is a wealth of material on Astrology. A possible starting point is *Cosmic Influences on Human Behaviour* by M. Gauquelin (Futura, 1976). On inward consciousness and meditation two recommended books are *The Only Revolution* by J. Krishnamurti in *The Second Penguin Krishnamurti Reader* (Penguin, 1973), and *The Buddha's Way* by H. Saddhatissa (Allen and Unwin, 1971). Also recommended is *Memories, Dreams and Reflections* by C.G. Jung (Fontana, 1967) and *The Book on the Taboo against Knowing Who You are* by A.W. Watts (Abacus, 1973).

Hazel Henderson's book *The Politics of the Solar Age* (New York, Doubleday/Anchor), is available from the Schumacher Book Service. On brain hemisphere function there is again a wealth of material but perhaps the best starting point is *The Psychology of Consciousness* by R. E. Ornstein (Harcourt Brace, 1977). James Lovelock's book *Gaia: A New Look at Life on Earth* was published by Oxford University Press in 1979.

There is, of course, by now a mass of material on the feminist movement and women's issues: an explosion of publication in the 1970s and 1980s that is itself a reflection of expanding New Age consciousness. A good general introduction is *Sweet Freedom: The Struggle for Women's Liberation* by Anna Coote and Beatrix Campbell (Picador). More theoretical is the Open University's *The Changing Experience of Women*, a collection of essays (Martin Robertson). Another overview is given in *Subject*

Women by Ann Oakley (Fontana). Worth a look at, too, is *Lifeways — Working with Family Questions*, edited by Gudrun Davy and Boris Voors (Hawthorn Press); note, particularly, Margli Matthews' essay on *The Meaning of Being a Mother Today*. But the best linkage of the women's movement with New Age consciousness we discovered was Rosemary Radford Ruether's *New Woman, New Earth: Sexist Ideologies and Human Liberation* (The Seabury Press, New York; available from the Schumacher Book Service).

On the American Indians, send a large stamped addresed envelope to the Public House Bookshop, 21 Little Preston Street, Brighton, BN1 2HQ, for their free catologue. The Onaway Trust, 275 Main Street, Shadwell, Leeds, publishes a quarterly magazine on news concerning the American Indians, together with background articles on their history and culture. Tim Macartney recommended to us *Seven Arrows* by Hyemeyohsts Storm (Ballantine Books, New York, 1972; distributed by Harper and Row).

Prana can be contacted at Tangelynen, Cwm Con, Newcastle Emlyn, Dyfed. Tapes of their chanting can be obtained by writing to Solar Sound Ltd, Llanrhystud, Dyfed (so far they have produced two tapes, First and Second Chants; a third tape is on the way). Ray and Mary Brooks have published a pamphlet *Spirit, Mind and Body: The Technique of Affirmation* available from Brick Kiln Farm, High Rougham, Bury St Edmunds, Suffolk. Details on Rebirthing and a British directory of Rebirthers can be obtained from The Rebirth Society, 21 Streets Heath, West End, Woking, Surrey. The most comprehensive book on the subject is *Rebirthing: The Science of Enjoying All your Life* by Jim Leonard and Phil Latu (Trinity Publications, 1636 North Curson Avenue, Hollywood, California 90046, USA).

For information on Green CND contact: John Marjoram, 23 Lower Street, Stroud, Gloucestershire, or CND Publications, 11 Goodwin Street, London N4 3HQ. *Embrace the Earth* is available from either address.

Fritz Schumacher's most famous book is, of course, *Small is Beautiful* (Abacus paperback). Sir George Trevelyan has written *A Vision of the Aquarian Age* (Coventry) and *Operation Redemption* (published Turnstone Press, which has a complete catalogue of New Age publications: write to Turnstone Press Ltd., Wellingborough, Northamptonshire). The Wrekin Trust, which arranges conferences and courses concerned with the evolution of consciousness and the deeper truths behind the work's religions, can be contacted at Dove House, Little Birch, Hereford HR2 8BB. Its director is Malcolm Lazarus.

Leopold Kohr's seminal work, *The Breakdown of Nations*, was first published in 1957. It is now available in paperback from Christopher Davies Publications Ltd., 4/5 Thomas Road, Swansea, as are his *The Overdeveloped Nations* and *Development Without Aid*. All these are also available from the Schumacher Book Service.

Illustration credits:

Front cover Martin W Roberts
Bristol Cancer Help Centre 79, 80
Jacqueline Capra 13
Ecoropa 27
Colin Harrison 14
Martin Haswell 79
Milton Keynes Development Corporation 98
Morgan Photographic 58
Resurgence 60, 110, 124
Martin W Roberts 33, 121, 123
Terence Soames (Cardiff) Ltd Photography 1, 2, 5, 7, 12, 18, 24, 26, 29, 32, 34, 36, 37, 38, 39, 40, 45, 46, 48, 52, 55, 63, 65, 67, 70, 71, 73, 74, 76, 79, 87, 90, 91, 92, 95, 96, 98, 102, 105, 107, 113, 116